What Do You Do With a Drunken Sailor?

Other Swordsmith Books

The 2002 Red Sox Fan Handbook
History of Windham County, Volume I
History of Windham County, Volume II
The Adult Student ss Guide
The Internet Guide for Seniors
The Internet Guide for Families
The New England Museum Guide
The Tri-State Museum Guide

see your bookseller for more information or order
from www.swordsmith.com

What Do You Do With a

Drunken Sailor?

Unexpurgated Sea Chanties

Compiled and Annotated by Douglas
Morgan

Swordsmith Books
Pomfret, Connecticut

A Swordsmith Book

Published by
Swordsmith Productions
PO Box 242
Pomfret, CT 06258
www.swordsmith.com

Printing history
First edition published in June 2002

ISBN: 1-931013-09-8

Edited by Leigh Grossman
Copyedited by Lesley McBain
Cover design by Elizabeth Glover

Swordsmith Books are distributed by
Weatherhill, 41 Monroe Turnpike, Trumbull, CT 06611,
(800)437-7840, fax (800)557-5601

Swordsmith Books is represented nationally by
Continental Sales, Inc., 213 West Main Street, Barrington, IL
60010, (847)381-6530, fax (847)382-0419

Printed in the U.S.A.
10 9 8 7 6 5 4 3 2 1

Dedicated to LCDR Robert F. "Mac" McBain,
USN, ret.

Also to Sharon, Barb, Paula, Sally, Skippy, Deedles,
Kathy, Carol, Kate, Virginia, Mary, Amy,
Claudette, Robin, Teri, Leslie . . . and others.

"Now seamen who spent their time in cargo-carrying sailing ships never heard a decent shanty; the words which sailor John put to them when unrestrained were the veriest filth."

—Master Mariner W. B. Whall

CONTENTS

INTRODUCTION

This book came about in a strange way. I've known Doug Morgan for upwards of ten years now, and edited his first book, the military thriller *Tiger Cruise*. Last winter, he and I were both at a literary convention when I got a call that my father-in-law, LCDR Robert F. McBain, had died suddenly. The rest of the convention was something of a blur, as writers and editors dropped by to pay their respects and the Swordsmith party planned for that Saturday night transformed into an impromptu wake. ("He wouldn't have wanted the beer to go to waste," commented more than one person.) I wrote a brief piece describing how much Mac's life had touched me and others who I knew, and somehow managed to read it out to the crowd of publishing professionals who had gathered. My wife had also written a piece about her father, which she couldn't bring herself to read out loud. Instead, she asked Doug to read it for her.

After he read out her recollections of LCDR McBain, Doug, who has a beautiful voice, broke into the Navy Hymn, joined by a number of former service members in the room. Pretty much everyone was crying by the time he finished. This was a wake, however, and there was a lot of beer in the room, and the point was to celebrate Mac's life and thirty-year Naval career, not just to mourn him. The Navy Hymn soon gave way to "What Do You Do with a Drunken Sailor" and "Frigging in the Rigging" and a dozen or so other songs.

About a month later I ran into Doug at another conference, and ended up taking him out to dinner. *Tiger Cruise* had just come out recently and was doing pretty well in terms of sales but the process of putting the book together—the book had been delayed for about six months by a particular Hollywood agent's pointless machinations, and plagued by a number of other glitches along the way—had taken a lot of the joy out of what had been a fun project, and strained a number of friendships. We decided to look for another project that would restore the kind of fun that *Tiger Cruise* had been when Doug was first writing it, and the talk drifted back to the previous month's wake, still very fresh in both our minds.

Well, Doug spent many years in the Navy before finishing up his doctorate and turning to—among other things—a writing career, and he's still never far from the sea, at least metaphorically. Soon the idea of this collection was born. There have been many collections of sea chanties, but very few of them print the chanties the way they are actually sung, or put them into the context of the Naval and maritime traditions in which they are created. Every one of these songs was actually sung at sea, on the ships where Douglas Morgan served. His marvelous annotations lay out the background, people, terms, and places that the songs celebrate, as well as showing how they still fit into today's Navy. Despite Doug's academic background, his annotations aren't dry commentaries on dead folklore; they are filled with jokes, intra-service barbs, variant songs, bizarre people, and everything else readers need to understand—or relive, for fellow sailors—what is still a vital, growing body of music, sung in hundreds of variants on hundreds of ships to this day.

This is not intended to be an exhaustive collection, but a sampling of some of the most interesting, most loved, and most important sea chanties—some dating from the age of sail, and some much newer. A number of them have never seen print before, and most of them have never been printed in their unbowdlerized versions.

LCDR McBain saw action in four wars—depending on how you count the Cuban Missile Crisis, which he was in the thick of. Douglas Morgan saw combat too, although he doesn't talk about it much. As this book goes to press Naval units are engaged in interdiction in the Persian Gulf and combat missions over Afghanistan. This book is a tribute to the Navy that each of them served in—a fine professional force, but one that doesn't believe in letting the beer go to waste.

—Leigh Grossman
April, 2002

HAUL AWAY JOE

When I was a little boy,
Or so my mother told me,
   Way haul away, we'll haul away, Joe!
That if I did not fuck the girls
My prick would go all moldy.
   Way haul away, we'll haul away, Joe!

  Chorus:
   To me way haul away, we'll haul and hang together!
      Way haul away, we'll haul away, Joe!
   To me way haul away, we'll haul for better weather!
      Way haul away, we'll haul away, Joe!

King Louis was the king of France
Afore the revolu-ti-on,
   Way haul away, we'll haul away, Joe!
But then he got his head cut off,
Which spoiled his constitu-ti-on.
   Way haul away, we'll haul away, Joe!

First I had a German girl
And she was fat and lazy.
   Way haul away, we'll haul away, Joe!

1

Then I had a English girl,
She damned near drove me crazy.
    Way haul away, we'll haul away, Joe!

Saint Patrick was an Irishman,
He came of decent people.
    Way haul away, we'll haul away, Joe!
He built a church in Dublin town,
And then he built the steeple.
    Way haul away, we'll haul away, Joe!

Ships in dock at Cardiff. From *Harper's New Monthly Magazine*, February 1877.

Once I was in Ireland
Digging turf and praties.
    Way haul away, we'll haul away, Joe!
And now I'm on a Yankee ship
Hauling on sheets and braces.
    Way haul away, we'll haul away, Joe!

Way haul away
We'll haul away the bowline
   Way haul away, we'll haul away, Joe!
Way, haul away
The packet is a-rollin'
   Way haul away, we'll haul away, Joe!

"HAUL AWAY JOE" is one of the tack and sheet chanties, used in pulling on lines. The lead singer, or chantyman, would sing out the verses, and the crew members working on the lines would join in with the chorus, using the rhythm of the song to time their efforts and insure that they all pulled as one. As recently as the late 1970s, the compiler of this collection heard "Haul Away Joe" used as a short-haul chanty for heaving on messenger lines during repping and unrepping ("underway replenishment"—refueling a ship at sea) aboard USS *Savannah* (AOR-4). In modern performances, it's usually kissing the girls that prevents the singer's lips from going moldy; the original singers had more explicit concerns and didn't hesitate to make them known.

The lists of girls of various nationalities that the sailor has been acquainted with float back and forth between "Haul Away Joe" and "Haul Away for Rosie":

Were you ever down on the Eastern Shore,
It really is a treat, Oh!
   Way, haul away, we'll haul away for Rosie
   Way, haul away, we'll haul away for Rosie, Oh.
Where the Baltimore whores in their purple drawers
Come runnin' out to greet you.
   Way, haul away, we'll haul away for Rosie
   Way, haul away, we'll haul away for Rosie, Oh.

Stanzas could be made up on the spot to fit circumstances or people:

You call yerself a second mate,
An' cannot tie a bowline;
You cannot even stand up straight
When the packet she's a rollin'.

Bowline (figs. 10–12).—Lay the end *a* of a rope over the standing part *b*. Form with *b* a bight *c* over *a*. Take *a* round behind *b* and

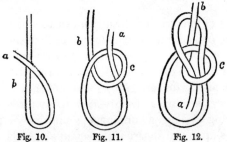

Fig. 10.   Fig. 11.   Fig. 12.

down through the bight *c*. This is a most useful knot employed to form a loop which will not slip.

A bowline. From *Encyclopedia Britannica*, 1892.

The first written version of "Haul Away Joe" dates from 1917. Prior to the development of folklore as an academic discipline, songs like this one had a furtive and largely unchronicled existence in the oral tradition. Fortunately, collectors in the early decades of the twentieth century were able to interview some of the surviving tall-ship sailors in retirement and record their songs for posterity. The publication of such a collection often marked a song's first appearance in written form.

My prick would go all moldy. "Prick" has been the common English word for "penis" since at least Shakespeare's time—Mercutio, speaking of the time of day in *Romeo and Juliet,* says "the bawdy hand of the dial is now upon the prick of noon." By the 1880s the term "dick" (from Cockney rhyming slang) was starting to take over from the original.

4

We'll haul for better weather. Weather is another common topic on shipboard, after girls and whiskey—but this book is not about weather.

Digging turf and praties. A line that refers to the peat bogs which supplied the Irish peasantry with much of their fuel, and the potatoes which provided them with food. As bad as sailing before the mast could be (as Samuel Johnson said, "Going to sea is going to prison, with a chance at drowning besides") it was better than starving in Ireland.

From *Harper's New Monthly Magazine*, March 1879.

From *Harper's New Monthly Magazine*, March 1877.

NEW YORK GIRLS

Chorus:
Away, Santy,
My dear Annie!
Oh, you New York girls,
Can't you dance the polka?

As I walked out on South Street, a fair maid I did meet.
She asked me then to see her home—she lived on Fourteenth
   Street.
   Away, Santy,
   My dear Annie!
   Oh, you New York girls,
   Can't you dance the polka?

I said, "My dear young lady, I'm a stranger here in town.
I left my ship just yesterday, from Liverpool I was bound."

I took her out to Tiffany's, I spared her no expense—
I bought her two gold earrings, they cost me fifty cents.

She said, "Come with me, dearie, I'll stand you to a treat.
I'll buy you rum and brandy, dear, and tab-nabs for to eat."

And when we got to Fourteenth Street we stopped at
    Number Four.
Her mother and her sisters came to greet her at the door.

"Her mother and her sisters came to greet her at the door." From *Harper's New
Monthly Magazine*, April 1853.

Then when we got inside the house the drinks was handed
    round.
That liquor was so awful strong, my head went round and
    round.

When the drinking it was over, we straight to bed did go,
And little did I ever think she'd prove my overthrow.

When I awoke next morning, I had an aching head,
And there was I, Jack-all-alone, stark naked on the bed.

My gold watch and my pocketbook and my lady friend
  were gone,
And there was I without a stitch or cent to call me own.

I looked all around the room, but nothing could I see
But a lady's shift and apron, not worth a damn to me.

Everything was silent, the hour was eight o'clock.
I put the shift and apron on and headed for the dock.

My shipmates seeing me come aboard, these words to me
  did say—
"Well, well, old chap, you've lost your cap since last you
  went away."

"Is this the new spring fashion that the ladies wear ashore?
Where is the shop you got it in? Have they got any more?"

The Old Man cried, "Why Jack, my boy, I'm sure I could
  have found
A better suit than that, by far, to buy for eighty pounds."

So come all you bully sailormen, take warning when ashore,
Or else you'll meet some charming girl who's nothing but a
  whore.

Your hard-earned cash will disappear, your rig and boots as
  well,
For Yankee girls are tougher than the other side of Hell.

THERE'S A JOKE about how to guarantee yourself a good time on liberty: First, go up on deck, take out your wallet, and throw all your money over the side. Then go below to your berthing quarters. Take an old sock and put it in your mouth. Now slam your dick in your locker door. Bang your head against the bulkhead four or five times. Now hit your rack and go to sleep.

In the morning: Your head hurts, your dick hurts, your mouth tastes like shit, your money is gone, and you can't remember leaving the ship. You *must* have had a good time!

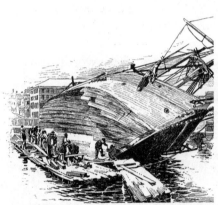

Careening ship. From *The Century Magazine*, August 1890.

"New York Girls" is a capstan shanty. The capstan was usually a vertical shaft with spokes that men would push to apply force to the cable used when hauling up the anchor, raising boats, and careening ship. These tasks could take hours of hard, monotonous work. Like many songs and yarns, the shanty also functions as a cautionary tale: A sailor ashore in unfamiliar territory, with the pay for an entire voyage burning a hole in his pocket, is an easy mark for the unscrupulous. The theme of the defrauded and embarrassed sailor appears in a number of songs, of which this is one of the liveliest.

"Away, Santy, my dear Annie!" This is probably a reference to the Mexican dictator and general Antonio Lopez de Santa Anna (1794–1876). A major player in Mexican politics during the middle years of the nineteenth century, Santa Anna first came to the attention of the American public during the Texas revolution of 1835, as the villain of the piece in the battles of Goliad and the Alamo before his defeat by Sam Houston at San Jacinto. He made the news in the United States a second time during the U.S.-Mexican War of 1846-1848, as the commander of the defeated Mexican forces—although in the short-haul chanty "The Plains of Mexico" he emerges as victorious:

> Santy Anno won the day.
> > Away, Santy Anno!
> He won the battle of Monterey
> > All on the plains of Mexico!

> Mexico, Mexico—
> Away, Santy Anno!
> Mexico is a place I know—
> All on the plains of Mexico!

There are sexual stanzas in "The Plains of Mexico," too:

> Them Spanish girls I do adore
> > Away, Santy Anno!
> They'll suck you dry and ask for more
> > All on the plains of Mexico.

General Santa Anna. From *History of the United States of America*, by Henry C. Watson, 1879.

11

When I was a young man in my prime,
Away, Santy Anno!
I'd knock them Scouse girls two at a time.
All on the plains of Mexico!

("Scouse" is slang for a Liverpudlian; that is, a person from Liverpool, England. "Liverpool scouse"—a hearty beef and potato stew, heavy on the potatoes—is a local specialty dish.)

But now my hair is turning grey
Away, Santy Anno!
They look at me and run away
All on the plains of Mexico.

How a Mexican general came to play such a prominent role in the seafaring musical tradition is somewhat of a puzzler. One theory is that he got a boost from Saint Anne, the patron saint of Breton sailors. It's possible that nineteenth-century Yankee sailors conflated memories of

Vera Cruz, Mexico, during the Mexican War. From *History of the United States of America*, by Henry C. Watson, 1879.

encounters with Breton sailors swearing by their patron *Sainte Anne* with then-current news stories about General Santa Anna.

Santa Ana himself eventually moved to Staten Island, where he helped introduce chewing gum to the United States.

Can't you dance the polka? The Bohemian folk dance known as the polka didn't become current in English-speaking circles until the 1840s—about the time of the U.S.-Mexican War.

Liverpool. Liverpool, on the southwest coast of England at the mouth of the Mersey River, was a major point of departure for ships sailing across the North Atlantic. The city, and especially its waterfront, make frequent appearances in sea chanties and sailors' yarns. The port of New York was in many ways its opposite number on the other side of the Atlantic, especially with regard to the hazards facing newly paid sailors. The unlucky narrator of "New York Girls" is a sailor out of Liverpool.

She lived on Fourteenth Street. There's nothing magical about the address: the young lady is reported to reside lots of places in various versions, including but not limited to Bleecker Street and Houston Street. The sailor sometimes starts at South Street, sometimes on Broadway, sometimes in the Bowery.

I took her out to Tiffany's. This famous New York jewelry firm has been in existence for well over a century and half, beginning in 1837 as the stationary and fancy goods emporium of Tiffany & Young. The first Tiffany's catalogue came out in 1845, within a couple of years of both the U.S.-Mexican War and the polka vogue. At least nobody at Tiffany's would have tried to cheat our hapless young sailor; from the first, the store featured a fixed, non-negotiable selling price on the goods it offered. The firm was renamed "Tiffany & Co." in 1853, and still does business under that name today.

The hour was eight o'clock. Eight o'clock was also eight bells of the morning watch, and the start of the forenoon watch—the beginning of the ship's working day.

DOUGLAS MORGAN

The Old Man. The ship's captain. The term has nothing to
do with actual age. In an era
when boys went to sea in their
teens or even younger, the
ship's captain might still be in
his twenties.

Come all ye bully sailormen.
"Bully," in this context, is a
term of approval—see also
Theodore Roosevelt's use of
"Bully!" as a favored interjec-
tion, and the word's more
ironic use in "The Ballad of
Eskimo Nell":

Captain Porter, circa 1812. From *Harper's New Monthly Magazine*, August 1859.

> She got to her feet and she looked so sweet;
> "Bully," she said, "for you.
> But I might have guessed it was about the best
> You Yankee simps could do."

The first written version of "New York Girls" dates from 1882.
Alternate endings include:

> I joined a Yankee bloodboat,
> And sailed away next morn.
> Don't ever fuck with New York girls—
> You're safer off Cape Horn.

(A "bloodboat" was a ship with notoriously brutal discipline. Even
that, apparently, was preferable to an entanglement with one of New
York's Fairest.)

14

BARNACLE BILL
(ABLE BROWN THE SAILOR)

"Who's that knocking on my door?
Who's that knocking on my door?
Who's that knocking on the door?"
Cried the fair young maiden.

"It's only me from over the sea,"
Said Barnacle Bill the Sailor.
"I'm hard to windward and hard to lee,"
Said Barnacle Bill the Sailor.
"I've just arrived upon the shore,
And this is what I'm looking for:
A jade, a maid or even a whore,"
Said Barnacle Bill the Sailor.

"Are you young and handsome, sir?
Are you young and handsome, sir?
Are you young and handsome, sir?"
Cried the fair young maiden.

"I'm old and rough and dirty and tough,"
Says Barnacle Bill the Sailor,

DOUGLAS MORGAN

"I never can get drunk enough,"
Says Barnacle Bill the Sailor,
"I drinks my whiskey when I can
Drinks it from an old tin can,
For whiskey is the life of man,"
Says Barnacle Bill the Sailor.

"I'll come down and let you in,
I'll come down and let you in,
I'll come down and let you in,"
Cried the fair young maiden.

"Open the door and lie on the floor,"
Said Barnacle Bill the Sailor.
" 'Cause whattya think I came here for,"
Said Barnacle Bill the Sailor.

From *The Century Magazine,* February 1890.

16

"I'll spin you yarns and tell you lies,
I'll drink your grog and eat your pies,
I'll tear your dress and black your eyes,"
Said Barnacle Bill the Sailor.

"Oh, your whiskers scrape my cheeks,
Oh, your whiskers scrape my cheeks,
Oh, your whiskers scrape my cheeks,"
Cried the fair young maiden.

"I'm dirty and lousy and full of fleas,"
Said Barnacle Bill the Sailor.
"I stick my mast in who I please,"
Said Barnacle Bill the Sailor
"My flowing whiskers give me class,
The seahorses eat them instead of grass,
If they scrape your cheeks, they'll tickle your ass,"
Said Barnacle Bill the Sailor.

"Tell me that we soon shall wed!
Tell me that we soon shall wed!
Tell me that we soon shall wed!"
Cried the fair young maiden.

"You foolish girl, it's nothing but sport,"
Said Barnacle Bill the Sailor.
"And handsome girls is what I court,"
Said Barnacle Bill the Sailor.
"With my false heart and flattering tongue,
I fucks 'em all both old and young,
I fucks 'em all but marries none,"
Said Barnacle Bill the Sailor.

"When will I see you again?
When will I see you again?
When will I see you again?"
Cried the fair young maiden.

"Never no more, you fucking whore,"
Said Barnacle Bill the Sailor.
"For I'm a-sailing from the shore,"
Said Barnacle Bill the Sailor.
"I'm sailing away on another tack,
To give another fair maid a crack,
But keep it oiled 'til I come back,"
Said Barnacle Bill the Sailor.

BARNACLE BILL IS the name of the sailor in the version of this song that most of us heard in school. In other versions, the horny protagonist is sometimes Able Brown the Sailor (giving him the initials A. B. S., which also form the standard abbreviation for Able-Bodied Seaman); or, in British versions, Bollocky Bill. There are lots of other lines and rhymes in this song, which like many others can be expanded to fill the time at hand: "What if I should have a child?"/"I'll dig a ditch and bury the bitch. . . . " and so on. The first written version dates from 1927.

I'm hard to windward and hard to lee. A nautical joke. "Hard" is a rudder order. "Hard to windward" means turning the ship's wheel as far as it will go to the direction the wind is coming from. "Hard to lee" means turning the wheel as far as it will go away from the wind. This may also refer to the sailor's jumper trousers, which have a front flap held up with two vertical rows of buttons. These can be opened on the right or on the left. There's a joke in which a sailor opens his button fly on the right, screws a young lady, puts his piece away, buttons up, then unbuttons the other side and says, "Now I'll use the other one."

I'll drink your grog and eat your pies. Technically, "grog" refers to mixture of one part rum to two parts water, traditionally served out as a liquor ration on British ships. The ration was originally established in 1740 by Admiral Vernon—called "Old Grog" from the grogram cloak he habitually wore—and took its nickname from its inventor. (Grogram was a fabric of the period, a coarsely woven mixture of silk and wool.) By extension, "grog" has become nautical slang for booze of any kind. On a Navy base, for example, the store that sells beer, wine, and hard liquor is referred to as the "grog shop." As for eating the fair young maiden's pies . . . given that "pie," short for "hair pie," is a common slang term for the female genitalia, the sexual connotations are probably deliberate.

My flowing whiskers give me class. To quote the compiler of this book, "Sailors belong on ships, ships belong at sea, and beards belong on sailors." It's only since the latter part of the twentieth century that sailors have commonly gone clean-shaven; in earlier times, both beards and long hair were common. Sailors in the British and American wooden-ship navies braided their hair into tight pigtails and tarred them. In the nineteenth century the clipper ship sailors and the packet sailors could be distinguished from one another by their customary haircuts: the clipper-ship sailors, whose voyages could last for

Packet ship. From *Harper's New Monthly Magazine*, February 1877.

several months, wore their hair long; but the "packet rats," whose back-and-forth voyages across the northern Atlantic lasted only about a month in either direction, wore their hair close-cropped.

"Barnacle Bill" also exists in a simpler question-and-response version:

> "What's that running down my leg?
> What's that running down my leg?
> What's that running down my leg?"
> Cried the fair young maiden.
> "It's only a shot that missed your twat,"
> Said Barnacle Bill the Sailor.
> "It's only a shot that missed your twat,"
> Said Barnacle Bill the Sailor.

One of the rocks found on Mars by the Mars Lander was named "Barnacle Bill" by the scientists. Our boy certainly gets around. . . .

Hog-eye Man

Oh, the Hog-eye man is the man for me,
For he is blind and he cannot see.

> *Chorus:*
> With his Hog-eye, oh.
> Railroad nigger with his Hog-Eye,
> Row ashore with the Hog-Eye, Oh,
> All she wants is a Hog-Eye man!

Oh, Sally's in the garden picking peas,
The hair on her head hanging down to her knees.

Oh, the Hog-Eye man gave a fond look of love,
And it charmed Sally's heart that was pure as a dove.

Oh, Sally's in the parlor a-sitting on his knee,
A-kissing of the sailor who'd come o'er the sea.

Sally's in the garden sifting sand,
And the Hog-eye man sitting hand in hand.

Sally's in the garden picking peas,
With a little Hog-eye all sitting on her knees.

Sally's in the kitchen, punching duff,
And the cheeks of her ass going chuff, chuff, chuff.

Oh, in San Francisco, there she'll wait,
For the Hog-eye man to come through her gate.

Oh, and who's been here since I been gone,
Some big buck nigger with his sea-boots on.

Oh, a Hog-eye ship and a Hog-eye crew,
A Hog-eye mate and a skipper too.

EARLIEST WRITTEN VERSION 1922

In decades past, this long drag chanty—set to the tune of a lively reel—
was unsingable in polite company because of its explicit sexual language: "Hog-eye" was a slang term for the female genitalia. (A long
drag chanty was one used for hauling on long lines, or in tasks requir-
ing a long, steady pull rather than a series of short jerks.) In railroad
parlance, "hog-eye" was also a slang term for a locomotive engineer,
since the locomotive engine itself was often called a hog; the "railroad"
reference in this shanty may come from the intersection of two sets of
occupational slang. Alternatively, a "hog-eye" may have been a kind of
barge; but this interpretation remains controversial.

These days, the song's sexual content seems almost quaint, and you
could say "hog-eye" to your maiden aunt in church without getting
more than a puzzled smile. The song, however, remains unsingable in
public, this time because of its casual use of the word "nigger." The
unexpurgated lyrics are included in this collection as an indicator of
social change, and as a reminder that the nineteenth century merchant
marine was in fact a multiracial institution.

Some versions of the song use the phrase "railroad navvy" instead
of "railroad nigger"; "navvy" is British slang for a casual construction

laborer. It's even possible that "railroad navvy" may have been the original form, and that the alien term "navvy" was replaced with a word more comprehensible to American audiences.

A black sailor. From *Harper's New Monthly Magazine*, March 1857.

Sally's in the kitchen, punching duff. "Duff" is a boiled or steamed pudding made with dried fruit, popular on shipboard.. The word was originally an altered form of "dough," which suggests that Sally may actually be kneading bread—an activity more likely than making steamed pudding to impart the vigorous motion described in the song.

Cooks were required to whistle while making duff to prove that they weren't eating any of the fruit; this requirement exempted them from the normal prohibition on whistling aboard ship. ("Only cooks, bosun's mates, and queers whistle," as the saying went as recently as the mid-1980s.) The traditional reason given for the ban on whistling was that whistling on board ship would summon up an unwanted wind. With the change from wind to steam power, the reason given also changed. These days, new sailors are told that whistling sounds like a steam leak and is forbidden on that account. In fact, steam leaks sound nothing at all like a man whistling; but—like an unwanted wind in the days of sail—superheated steam escaping under high pressure is extremely dangerous, and the new hazard attached itself to the old superstition.

(Sailors, considered as a group, tend to be superstitious. Like authors, actors, and athletes—to name three other professions also highly prone to superstition—they're in a line of work where their success or failure, or even their survival, is to a large extent determined by forces beyond their control.)

From *Harper's New Monthly Magazine*, March 1858.

WHUP JAMBOREE

Now, my boys, be of good cheer,
For the Irish land will soon be near.
In a few more days we'll sight Cape Clear—
O Jenny keep your cunthole warm!

> *Chorus:*
> O jamboree, whup jamboree,
> You pigtail sailormen sheet her home behind!
> O jamboree, whup jamboree,
> O Jenny keep your cunthole warm!

Now the Pilot he looks out ahead,
With a hand in the chains and a-heaving on the lead,
And the Old Man shouts to wake the dead,
"Jenny keep your cunthole warm!"

And now we're past the Lizard Light,
And the Start Me buoys will heave in sight.
We'll soon be abreast of the Isle of Wight,
And it's Jenny keep your cunthole warm!

And when we reach those Blackwall docks,
The pretty young girls come down in flocks.

With their short-legged drawers and long tailed frocks—
Jenny keep your cunthole warm!

And when we walk down Limehouse way
Them pretty young girls will spend our pay
We won't get more 'til another day
Jenny keep your cunthole warm.

Limehouse, London. From *The Century Magazine*, December 1888.

And when I stand upon the shore,
I'll pack up my bag and go to sea no more.
I'll say farewell to my Limehouse whore.
And it's Jenny keep your cunthole warm!

A SONG THAT DISPENSES with coyness and innuendo in favor of undisguised sexual content, "Whup Jamboree" is another short haul chanty that's almost never heard in unbowdlerized form. In present-day performances and recordings, Jenny is often urged to keep her "ring-tail" warm—an exhortation that doesn't make much sense but at least has the virtue of avoiding outright obscenity. Another version of the chorus—"Come and get your oats, me son!"—takes the text even further from its bawdy origins.

In a few more days we'll sight Cape Clear. The ship in this version of "Whup Jamboree" is bound for England from the west. The first land sighted after making the Atlantic passage is Cape Clear: Cape Clear Island, Ireland's southernmost inhabited island, eight miles off the coast of West Cork. They take aboard a pilot in the very next verse, then proceed past other landmarks in order. The navigational details in songs like this can be varied to suit the voyage and the situation. The editor of this collection, while en route from Norfolk to Philadelphia to visit his girlfriend, once extemporized a version of "Whup Jamboree" using the landmarks and highway intersections along Route 13 on Maryland's Eastern Shore.

You pigtail sailormen sheet her home behind! A "pigtail sailor" is one with a long hair in a tarred queue, rather than the cropped hair of a packet rat. "Sheet her home behind" is an order to adjust the sail to the wind.

The Pilot he looks out ahead. The pilot isn't a regular member of the ship's crew, but an individual with current local knowledge of a particular channel or stretch of water, taken aboard when the ship enters the waters in question and dropped off again afterward.

A hand in the chains and a-heaving on the lead. A member of the crew standing on the chainplates between the shrouds forward. Casting the lead, that is, throwing a weighted sounding line to ascertain the depth of the water, is used in a piloting situation. The deepsea lead (sometimes called the "dipsy" lead) had wax or tallow in a hollow in the bottom to bring up a sample of the bottom: sand, shell, gravel, and so on,

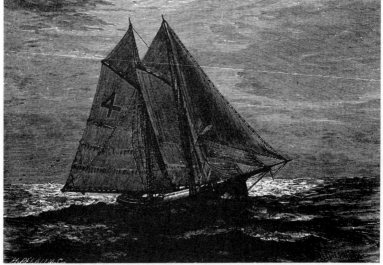

Pilot boat. From *Scribner's Magazine*, May 1888.

to give another indication of where on the chart the ship might be.

And now we're past the Lizard Light. The lighthouse at Lizard Point, in Cornwall (49° 57'.58 N/05° 12'.07 W) marks the southernmost point of mainland Britain.

We'll soon be abreast of the Isle of Wight. Having passed Lizard Point, the ship is now in the Bristol Channel, leading to the English Channel, the Thames, and London.

Blackwall Docks. The Blackwall Docks, in Wapping (now part of the Docklands area of London) were built in 1612–1614. The East India and West India Docks were later built nearby. The area was a major shipping and shipbuilding center throughout the eighteenth and nineteenth centuries, but fell into disuse after the Second World War. By 1988 all of the docks were closed.

I'll say farewell to my Limehouse whore. The Limehouse district was another part of the area near London that also held the Blackwall, East

India, and West India docks. The name came from the kilns, or lime-houses, for producing quicklime. From the sixteenth through the nineteenth century, Limehouse was also a center for shipbuilding; in the reign of King James I, it was estimated that mariners made up almost half the local population. In the 1890s, Chinese sailors working for the Blue Funnel Line made Limehouse the home of London's original Chinatown district. The area fell into decline in the mid-twentieth century, and by the 1970s was virtually derelict. In the 1980s, amid considerable controversy, it was redeveloped into an upscale business district.

From *Scribner's Monthly*, January 1880.

THE BIG WHEEL

A sailor told me before he died—
I never knew if the poor bastard lied—
That he had a bride with a cunt so wide
That she could never be satisfied.

So he built himself a big fucking wheel;
Bolted on a big prick of steel;
Two brass balls he filled with cream;
And the whole damn thing was powered by steam.

And around and around went the big fucking wheel.
In and out went that big prick of steel.
In and out, until she cried,
"Enough, enough! I'm satisfied!"

But there was just one thing wrong with it:
That there was no stopping it,
'Til she was split from twat to tit
And the whole damn thing was covered in shit.

IT'S SAID THAT the difference between a sea story and a fairy tale is this:
a fairy tale begins with, "Once upon a time," and a sea story begins

with, "No shit, this is the truth." It's also said, in the Navy, that there is no such thing as the Fleet. They send you to Boot Camp, and once you graduate they send you away to Sea Story School for six years before sending you back to Boot Camp as an instructor.

What's certainly true is that storytelling has always played an important role in seafaring life. Some stories have an instructive purpose, telling of the dangers that await a careless or unwary sailor and offering exemplars of right and wrong behavior under extraordinary circumstances. These stories tend to be at least partly true. Other stories—like the one in this song—are told mainly for the sake of diversion, and are not required to be true at all, so long as they are entertaining.

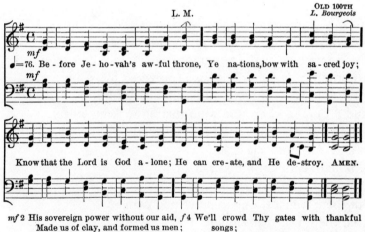

L. M.

OLD 100TH
L. Bourgeois

♩=76. Be - fore Je - ho - vah's aw - ful throne, Ye na - tions, bow with sa - cred joy;

Know that the Lord is God a - lone; He can cre - ate, and He de - stroy. AMEN.

mf 2 His sovereign power without our aid, *f* 4 We'll crowd Thy gates with thankful
Made us of clay, and formed us men ;   songs ;
And when like wandering sheep we   High as the heaven our voices raise ;
strayed,   And earth, with her ten thousand tongues,
He brought us to His fold again.   Shall fill Thy courts with sounding praise.

mf 3 We are His people, we His care, *f* 5 Wide as the world is Thy command,
Our souls, and all our mortal frame: Vast as eternity Thy love ;
cr What lasting honours shall we rear,   Firm as a rock Thy truth must stand,
Almighty Maker, to Thy Name?   When rolling years shall cease to move.
  I. Watts

Old One Hundredth. From *The Hymnal,* circa 1900.

The changeover from sail to steam began in the mid-nineteenth century, and was almost complete by the early decades of the twentieth century. This song was clearly inspired by the driving pistons of the great coal-powered reciprocating steam plants that drove vessels as late as the 1940s.

"The Big Wheel" is unusual among sea-songs in that the female protagonist dies. (Under most circumstances, sailors would consider this a pointless waste.) Also noteworthy is the fact that some versions of "The Big Wheel" can be sung to the psalm tune "Old Hundredth," which is also used for the Doxology ("Praise God from whom all blessings flow.")

From *The Century Magazine*, August 1890.

NORTH ATLANTIC SQUADRON

Chorus
Away, away with fife and drum,
Here we come, full of rum.
Looking for women who peddle their bum,
In the North Atlantic Squadron.

A-sailing up and down the coast,
Now, here's the thing we love the most:
To fuck the girls and drink a toast
In the North Atlantic Squadron.

Well, off the coast of Labrador,
We took on board a floating whore,
We fucked her forty times or more,
In the North Atlantic Squadron.

When we arrived in Montreal,
She spread her legs from wall to wall.
She took the Captain balls and all,
In the North Atlantic Squadron.

A-sailing up to Newfoundland,
Each sailor had his prick in his hand.
Oh say, my boys, can you make it stand?
In the North Atlantic Squadron.

And when our ship is in drydock,
The whores around us all do flock.
It's every man unfurl your cock,
In the North Atlantic Squadron.

Sailing in the North Atlantic. From *St. Nicholas,* February 1894.

THIS SONG DATES back to the First World War—or possibly earlier, since the North Atlantic Squadron in the American navy goes clear back to the American Civil War.

The high North Atlantic witnessed much naval action in World War Two as well. The fastest route from Europe to North America lay through those cold and stormy waters; German U-boats accordingly made the North Atlantic into a hunting ground, attacking merchant convoys from Canada and the United States on their way to England. The convoys transported supplies and war materiel that England needed in order to survive, and the Battle of the North Atlantic—as it came to be called—turned into a drawn-out affair where ultimate victory for one side or the other rested on the number of tons of merchant shipping sunk or safely brought into port.

Naval ships, usually destroyers, were responsible for the safety of the convoys. Even before Pearl Harbor and the formal declaration of war, the United States Navy had been informally at war in the North Atlantic. On April 10, 1941, USS *Niblack* used depth charges against a German U-boat while rescuing the crew of a torpedoed Dutch freighter—the first action taken by an American naval vessel against the Axis Powers. On September 4 of that same year, USS *Greer* was attacked, without ultimate success, by the German submarine U-652 while patrolling south of Iceland; the incident caused President Roosevelt to order US naval vessels to attack any ship that threatened American shipping or any foreign shipping under American escort. And on the thirty-first of October, 1941, the destroyer USS *Reuben James* was torpedoed and sunk with its crew of 115 by the U-552 while escorting a convoy out of Halifax, Nova Scotia, thus becoming the first United States vessel destroyed by the Axis powers.

This version of "The North Atlantic Squadron" contains several Canadian verses, and the tune is the same as the Salvation-Army-style "temperance" parody, "Away, Away With Rum, By Gum!"

A whaling expedition. From *St. Nicholas*, March 1894.

OFF TO SEA NO MORE

When first I landed in Liverpool, I went upon a spree.
Me money, alas, I spent it fast, got drunk as drunk could be.
And when me money was all gone 'twas then that I wanted
more,
But a man must be blind to make up his mind to go to sea
once more.

> *Chorus:*
> Once more, boys, once more, go to sea once more—
> But a man must be blind to make up his mind
> To go to sea once more.

I spent the night with Angeline, too drunk to roll in bed.
Me watch was new and me money too; in the morning with
them she fled.
And as I walked the streets about, then shouted out every
whore,
"There goes Jack Rat, the poor sailor man, he must go to
sea once more!"

And as I walked the streets about, I met with Rapper
Brown.
I asked him for to sign me on and he looked at me with a
frown.

He says, "Last time you were paid off, with me you'd chalk
  no score.
But I'll give ye a chance and I'll take yer advance and I'll
  send you to sea once more."

He shipped me on board a bold whaling ship bound for the
  arctic seas,
Where the cold wind blows over ice and snow and Jamaica
  rum would freeze;
But hardest to bear I'd no foul weather gear, for I'd spent all
  my money on shore—
'Twas then that I wished that I was dead and could go to
  sea no more.

Sometimes we're catching whales, my lads, sometimes we're
  catching none,
With a twenty foot oar all in my hand from four o'clock in
  the morn.
And when the shades of night come down then I lean on my
  weary oar—
'Tis then that I wish that I was dead and could go to sea no
  more.

So come all ye bold sea-faring men who listen to my song.
When you come back from those long trips I'll have you not
  go wrong.
Take my advice, drink no strong drink, don't go sleeping
  with them whores;
Get married instead and spend all night in bed and go to sea
  no more.

OUR LUCKLESS SAILOR lands in Liverpool . . . and loses his shirt and his pay for the voyage yet again, this time in the bed of the lovely Angeline. But Brown the shipping agent has a solution to the young man's problems: signing on as crew for an arctic whaling voyage.

With me you'd chalk no score. The barkeep/boarding master advances the sailor the price of food, drink, and lodging against his pay for the coming voyage. Our protagonist has been a thrifty lad and not run up a tab (marked on a chalkboard behind the bar)—which doesn't please the shipping agent because Jack isn't in his debt. It is possible that Angeline and Brown were in cahoots, to rob Jack and force him to quickly sign up on another ship through Brown's services.

I'll take yer advance. Sailors would be paid a month's advance for their coming voyage, presumably to buy clothing and supplies, send money to their wives, and settle any outstanding business. Often, the sailors took credit from boarding-masters or crimps, and the boarding-master

On board a North Atlantic whaler. From *The Century Magazine*, August 1890.

received the advance to pay back the debt. The part of the voyage during which the sailor was paying off the advance was called the "dead horse." In this case, Brown the shipping agent is taking the sailor's advance pay in return for finding him a berth.

Jamaica rum would freeze. Rum, usually in the form of grog—rum cut with water—was the traditional sailor's tipple. Like its British counterpart, the American navy had a rum ration; while that practice was ended in 1862, the Navy still remained "wet" until Secretary of the Navy Josephus Daniel put an end to all alcohol on shipboard in 1914. Josephus Daniel is also famous for declaring in 1922: "Nobody now fears that a Japanese fleet could deal an unexpected blow on our Pacific possessions. Radio makes surprise impossible." His memory is not loved in the Fleet.

I'd no foul weather gear. Our narrator lacks the proper clothing for a voyage above the Arctic Circle—heavy woolen garments, mostly, since wool has the useful property of remaining warm even when wet. Along with all his other problems, he's now a prime candidate for hypothermia. The money from his advance, which should theoretically have gone toward outfitting him, went to Brown the shipping agent instead.

Sailors in foul weather gear. From *The Century Magazine,* December 1891.

From *Harper's New Monthly Magazine*, October 1858.

PADDY LAY BACK

'Twas on a cold and dreary morning in December,
     (December!)
When all of me money it was spent.
     (Spent, spent!)
Just where it went I couldn't quite remember,
     (Remember!)
So down to the shipping office I went.
     (Went, went!)

     Chorus:
     Oh, Paddy lay back,
          (Paddy lay back!)
     Take in the slack,
          (Take in the slack!)
     Take a turn around the capstan,
     Heave a pawl!
          (Heave a pawl!)
     About ship's stations, boys, be handy!
          (Be handy!)
     We're bound for Valparaiso 'round the Horn!

That day there was a great demand for sailors,
For the colonies, for 'Frisco and for France.

Southern European dock, circa 1890. From *The Century Magazine*, April 1890.

So I shipped aboard a Limey bark, the *Hotspur*;
Got paralytic drunk on my advance.

'Twas on the quarter deck that first I spied them,
Such a lubberly lot I'd never seen before.
For the captain had shipped a shanghaied crew of Dutchmen
That made my poor old eyes feel sick and sore.

There was Spaniards an' Dutchmen an' Rooshians,
An' Johnny Crapoos just across from France.
And most of them could speak no word of English,
But answered to the name of "Month's Advance!"

Now some of the crew had started on for drinking,
And I myself was heavy on the booze,
So on my old sea chest I sat a-thinking
That I would go below and take a snooze.

I knew that in my box I had a bottle;
By the boarding-master 'twas put there.
I wanted something for to wet me throttle
Something for to drive away dull care.

So down upon my knees I went like thunder
And put me hand to the bottom of me box.
And what then was my pure surprise and wonder
To find nothing but a bottled cure for pox.

I asked the mate then which watch was mine-o;
He quickly told me which watch was which;
Then he knocked me down and kicked me hard astern-o,
Called me a dirty, lousy son of a bitch.

Douglas Morgan

I quickly made me mind up that I'd jump her;
I'd leave the bugger and get a job ashore.
I swum across the Bay and went and left her,
And in the English Bar I found a whore.

But Jimmy the Crimp he knew a thing or two, sir,
And soon he'd shipped me outward bound again
On a Limey to the Chinchas for guano,
And soon was I a-roaring this refrain:

> *Chorus:*
> Oh, Paddy lay back,
>   (Paddy lay back!)
> Take in the slack,
>   (Take in the slack!)
> Take a turn around the capstan,
> Heave a pawl!
>   (Heave a pawl!)
> About ship's stations, boys, be handy!
>   (Be handy!)
> We're bound for Valparaiso 'round the Horn!

From *The Century Magazine*, March 1890.

ANOTHER CAPSTAN CHANTY, this one dating from 1898 in written form, "Paddy Lay Back" is distinguished by the command in the chorus to "heave a pawl!" A pawl is part of a ratchet device which allows the capstan to turn in only one direction. Our sailor-narrator is once more broke and out of work, and returns perforce to the only trade he knows. In sea songs of the period, Irish were commonly called "Paddy." In shore songs they were more often called "Pat." Both are short for the common name "Patrick," patron saint of Ireland.

We're bound for Valparaiso 'round the Horn. The city of Valparaiso, Chile, was a popular destination for sailors in the nineteenth century—Herman Melville devotes an entire chapter of *Moby-Dick* to a discussion of its tawdry charms. It's the first decent harbor on the west coast of South America after rounding the Horn. "Valpo," as it's called, is still a popular liberty port. The first time the editor of this collection arrived in Valparaiso, his ship anchored out (i.e., dropped anchor but did not tie up to a pier.) That night, a little man came out in a rowboat and tossed packs of business cards bound by rubber bands onto the decks of all the moored ships, advertising "Nice girls to serve you any time."

I shipped aboard a Limey bark. Or, in some versions, a "lime-juice bark"—in any case, a British ship. In 1795, James Lind confirmed that the juice of limes or lemons, taken regularly, acted as a preventative for scurvy, the vitamin-C deficiency disease that until then had been a major limiting factor on the length of time a ship could spend underway. The British Navy promptly began issuing a regular ration of lime juice to its sailors, an innovation that allowed its ships to remain at sea for long periods of time and—by making possible an effective blockade of the French ports—contributed to the British victory against Napoleon. English sailors have been known as "limeys" ever since.

A lubberly lot. The "lubber line" is the fixed line on the front of the binnacle—the housing for the ship's compass—that marks the center line of the ship itself. To steer the ship, you line up the floating lines on the compass card with the lubber line. A land lubber is someone who points the lubber line toward land.

The captain had shipped a shanghaied crew of Dutchmen. The "Dutchmen" may have been actual sailors from the Low Countries, or they may have been Germans from Kiel or Hamburg. In any case, they were aboard unwillingly: to "shanghai" a sailor was to drug him and haul him aboard ship, then leave port before he came to. Ships bound on the long voyages to Shanghai in the Far East were so notorious for getting their crews in this way that the city lent its name to the practice.

Predictably, the shanty tradition is rich in cautionary tales of "the old Shanghai game." The song "Liverpool Judies" features a sailor-victim:

> The next I remember, I woke in the morn
> On a three skys'l yarder bound south round Cape Horn.
> With an old suit of oilskins and two pairs of socks
> And a bloomin' great head and a dose of the pox.

The song "Larry Mar" warns sailors of a tavern where the proprietor and his wife are playing the game:

> A hell-ship she was short o' hands,
> Of full red-blooded tars,
> And Missus an' Larry would prime the beer
> In the big five-gallon jar.

> Shellbacks and farmers just the same
> Walked in to Larry Mar's,
> Then sailed away around Cape Horn,
> Helped by the big stone jar.

The drugs used, when normal alcohol didn't suffice, were often chloral hydrate (the active ingredient in the classic Mickey Finn), or nicotine. Where those wouldn't serve, a blackjack would. A blackjack—often called a "life preserver"—was a common sailor's weapon, usually made from a small bag filled with lead shot and attached to a cord handle. The knots and fancywork on these weapons, done during the long hours at sea, could be quite elaborate.

An' Johnny Crapoos just across from France. "John (or Jean) Crapaud" was a common slang term for a French sailor—*crapaud*, or "toad," refers to the supposed French fondness for eating frogs and snails and similar un-English dishes. The scarcely veiled hostility to all things French is probably a relic of the period during the eighteenth and early nineteenth century when England and France contested for military and naval superiority.

I asked the mate then which watch was mine-o. Along with foul weather and boredom, the sailor's life at sea was characterized by exhausting, backbreaking work. Wet canvas is heavy, the yards could weigh a ton or more, and all would have to be moved with human muscle power.

The ship's crew (other than idlers like the carpenter and cook, who would stand no watches) was divided into two groups, the port and

Sailors in action on the USS *Wyoming*, 1863. From *The Century Magazine*, April 1892.

starboard watches. Each four hours one or the other group would be expected to be on deck, working the sails, pumping, steering, standing lookout, and performing the other tasks that keep a ship on top of the water and making way for its destination. All-hands evolutions for such tasks as raising the anchor or shortening sail would require both watch sections. Watch-and-watch means working four hours on and four off. Off-watch men could be required to mend clothing, paint, caulk, rub down spun yarn, or otherwise make themselves useful.

Every half hour, the mate of the watch would turn the sandglass that counted the hours, and strike the ship's bell, from once to eight times. At eight bells, the port watch section would relieve the starboard, or vice versa, and the process would continue with one bell. The sandglass would measure from noon to noon, since it's fairly easy to determine noon at sea: it's the moment when the sun is due north, due south, or directly overhead.

Warships could have more than two watch sections, since they were heavily overmanned compared to merchants. Each gun took a crew of six to man it, and these men were available when the ship wasn't fighting.

And in the English Bar I found a whore. These days, in almost any port in the world, you'll find a Texas Bar or a Hotel New York somewhere on the waterfront: generally a pretty tough place, the sort of joint where they frisk you on the way in, and if you aren't carrying a gun or a knife they give you one so you'll start even. In earlier years, almost every waterfront boasted of an "English Bar," where sailors could find what they wanted.

Jimmy the Crimp. A crimp (the word dates to the seventeenth century) would get seamen to desert from one ship in order to sign on another in return for a reward from the receiving ship, or would turn over men to a press gang for head money. The port of San Francisco, home of Larry Mar and Shanghai Brown, was notorious for its crimps in the late nineteenth and early twentieth centuries, where the going rate for a sailor was $30 plus expenses. Sometimes the crimp would get the sailor's first month's pay as his reward for supplying hands. The seaman might be unconscious while all this was going on. Crimping was a felony in England.

On a Limey to the Chincas for guano. The Chincas Islands, near Callao in Peru, were a major source of bird droppings, or guano, which was dug up by the ton and exported for use as fertilizer and in the manufacture of explosives. This was a lucrative trade during the age of sail, for all that it was a nasty job.

From *Scribner's Monthly*, December 1879.

From *Harper's New Monthly Magazine*, March 1858.

THE BALTIMORE SHANTY

He kissed her on the face,
And the crew began to roar:
    "Oh, oh, up she goes! We're bound for Baltimore!"
Then he kissed her on the nose,
And the crew began to roar:
    "Oh, oh, up she goes! We're bound for Baltimore!"

    Chorus:
    No more, no more, we go to sea no more.
    As soon we reach the town tonight,
    We're leaving for the shore.

Then he kissed her on the lips,
And the crew began to roar:
    "Oh, oh, up she goes! We're bound for Baltimore!"
Then he kissed her on the neck,
And the crew began to roar:
    "Oh, oh, up she goes! We're bound for Baltimore!"

    No more, no more, we go to sea no more.
    As soon we reach the town tonight,
    We're leaving for the shore.

Then he kissed her on the tit,
And the crew began to roar:
>"Oh, oh, up she goes! We're bound for Baltimore!"

And he kissed her on the cunt,
And the crew began to roar.
>"Oh, oh, up she goes! We're bound for Baltimore!"

>No more, no more, we go to sea no more.
>As soon we reach the town tonight,
>We're leaving for the shore.

From *Harper's New Monthly Magazine,* August 1881.

A SIMPLE PROGRESSION SONG, "The Baltimore Shanty" is noteworthy mostly because—unlike its politer cousins—the catalog of kisses doesn't confine itself to the parts of the young lady normally kept on public view.

We're bound for Baltimore! The port city of Baltimore, Maryland—located on Chesapeake Bay at the mouth of the Patapsco River—has been a major shipping center since before the American Revolution. Fort McHenry, of "Star Spangled Banner" fame, guards Baltimore Harbor. As recently as the late 1970s, the city's waterfront district, known colloquially as "the Block," was notorious for its rowdy night life. These days, however, Baltimore's old waterfront red-light district has suffered the same fate as London's Docklands and New York City's Times Square: cleaned out, cleaned up, renamed, and redeveloped.

Steamship and waterspout. From *Harper's New Monthly Magazine*, March 1858.

BALTIMORE WHORES

There were four whores of Baltimore,
Drinking the blood-red wine,
And all their conversation was,
"Yours is smaller than mine."

> *Chorus:*
> To me roly-poly tickle me holey,
> Smell of me slimy slew,
> And drag your nuts across me guts—
> I'm one of the whorey crew.

"You're a liar," said the first whore.
"Mine's as big as the air.
The birds fly in, the birds fly out,
And never touch a hair."

> *Alternate Chorus:*
> So swab the decks, me hearties,
> Sluice them down with brine,
> Lay to the oars, you sons of whores,
> Yours is smaller than mine.

"You're a liar," said the second,
"Mine's as big as the sea.
The ships sail in, the ships sail out,
And never trouble me."

To me roly-poly tickle me holey,
Smell of me slimy slew,
And drag your nuts across me guts—
I'm one of the whorey crew.

"You're a liar," said the third whore.
"Mine's as big as the moon.
The men jump in, the men jump out
And never touch the womb."

So swab the decks, me hearties,
Sluice them down with brine,
Lay to the oars, you sons of whores,
Yours is smaller than mine.

"Lay on the oars, you sons of whores. . . ." From *The Century Magazine*, August 1890.

"You're a liar," said the last whore.
"Mine's the biggest of all.
The fleet sailed in on the first of June
And didn't come out 'til fall."

> To me roly-poly tickle me holey,
> Smell of me slimy slew,
> And drag your nuts across me guts—
> I'm one of the whorey crew.

NEW YORK HAS ITS New York Girls, Liverpool has its Liverpool Judies, and Baltimore . . . well, unfortunately for its good musical reputation, the city rejoices in a name that rhymes easily with "whore." Chantymen—and lovers of lewd songs in general—took ample advantage of the fact. The Baltimore whores in this song may or may not wear purple drawers, but they're clearly as hard-boiled as they come.

So anyway, this sailor comes ashore on liberty. He's been at sea for about six months, and he's ready for a good time. So he heads straight to the first whorehouse on the Block, walks in, and says to the madame, "I want your toughest girl and two beers."

"Right," says the madame. "You'll want Rosie, then. She's the toughest whore in the world. First room at the top of the stairs."

The sailor pays and goes up, and pretty soon the door opens and in comes this girl with a bottle of beer in each hand. She puts down the beers, whips off her kimono, and gets on the floor on her hands and knees.

"Wait a minute," says Jack. "I want you in the bed, on your back, the old-fashioned way."

"Anything you say, sport," says Rosie. "I just thought you might want to open them beers first."

DOUGLAS MORGAN

Lay to the oars, you sons of whores, Yours is smaller than mine. These lines are taken from the typical exhortations of a boatsteerer, or coxswain, to the boat's crew. They're both a statement of literal fact—the single sweep oar used for steering the boat was in fact larger than the paired oars used for rowing it—and a sexual taunt.

From *Harper's New Monthly Magazine*, December 1852.

FRIGGING IN THE RIGGING

'Twas on the good ship Venus,
By Christ you should have seen us—
The figurehead was a whore in bed
And the mast a throbbing penis.

> *Chorus:*
> Frigging in the rigging, frigging in the rigging,
> Frigging in the rigging, there was fuck-all else to do.

The captain of that lugger,
He was a dirty bugger.
He wasn't fit to shovel shit
From one place to another.

The bosun's name was Carter,
A very musical farter.
He could fart anything from "God Save the King"
To Beethoven's "Moonlight Sonata."

The snottie was a chipper
Pernicious little nipper.
They stuffed his ass with broken glass
And circumcised the skipper.

An officer and midshipman. From *St. Nicholas*, October 1902.

The captain's name was Morgan;
By Christ he was a gorgon,
And every day sweet tunes he'd play
On his reproductive organ.

The captain's wife was Charlotte;
She was a natural harlot.
All through the night her thighs shone white,
By morning they were scarlet.

The cook's name was O'Malley;
He didn't dilly-dally.
He shot his bolt with such a jolt
It whitewashed half the galley.

The first mate's name was Andy;
By Christ he had a dandy,
'Til they crushed his cock with broken rock
For coming in the brandy.

The captain's daughter Mabel,
Lay on the wardroom table,
And all the crew would come and screw
As oft as they were able.

The captain's other daughter
Fell in the deep sea water.
Delighted squeals revealed the eels
Had found her sexual quarter.

The engineer was Cooper;
By Christ he was a trooper.
He jerked and jerked until he worked
Himself into a stupor.

DOUGLAS MORGAN

The coxswain's name was Hopper;
By Christ he had a whopper—
Twice 'round the deck, once 'round his neck,
Then up his ass for a stopper.

The ship's dog's name was Rover;
The whole crew turned him over.
They ground and ground that faithful hound
From Shanghai back to Dover.

The ship's cat's name was Kitty;
Her hole was black and shitty.
But shit or not, she had a twat,
And the Captain knew no pity.

'Twas in the Adriatic,
Where the water's almost static,
That the rise and fall of ass and ball
Was almost automatic.

Palace of Diocletian, Spalato, on the Adriatic. From *The Century*, April 1895.

What Do You Do with a Drunken Sailor?

Each sailor lad's a brother
To each and every other.
We take great pains at our daisy chains
Whilst writing home to mother.

The docks in Buenos Aires. From *St. Nicholas,* July 1903.

On the trip to Buenos Aires,
We buggered all the fairies.
We got the syph at Tenerife,
And the clap in the Canaries.

And when we reached our station,
And to our great elation
The ship was sunk in a sea of spunk
From mutual masturbation.

67

FRIG: *v.i.* meaning "to masturbate (another)." From the Middle English *fryggen*, to wiggle.

If songs like "Barnacle Bill" and "The Hog-Eye Man" celebrate the sexual voracity of a sailor on shore leave, songs like this one reflect the other face of seafaring life: long months or even years at sea, with few avenues of sexual release beyond homoeroticism, masturbation, and lurid fantasy.

The captain of that lugger. A "lugger" is a small fishing or coasting boat. If the Good Ship *Venus* is meant to be something quite a bit larger, as implied by its possession of a figurehead and by its varied ports of call, then referring to it as a lugger is meant as an insult. Calling a vessel that's properly a ship a "boat" is always insulting. In one of the ballads about the sinking of USS *Cumberland* by CSS *Virginia*—formerly USS *Merrimack*—*Virginia*'s captain is made to say, "Haul down your flying colors or I'll sink your Yankee boat." (Similarly, in the *Star Trek* episode "The Trouble with Tribbles," the Klingons insult the starship *Enterprise*, and start a bar fight, by referring to the *Enterprise* as a garbage scow.)

A very musical farter. Possibly even the equal of Joseph Pujol, *Le Pétomane*. Pujol, born in Marseilles, France, in 1857, achieved fame and fortune on the Parisian stage by virtue of his ability to take in as much as two quarts of air through his anus and expel it at will. Over

Luggers on the Mississippi. From *St. Nicholas*, January 1894.

A frigate bringing in prize ships. From *The Century Magazine*, November 1890.

the course of a 90-minute act, Pujol would use his skill at controlled farting to blow out candles, play popular tunes, and even do impressions of celebrities of the day. He was more popular than Sarah Bernhardt, if ticket sales are a judge.

The snottie was a chipper/Pernicious little nipper. A "snottie" was a midshipman. In the age of sail, the training of a naval officer began in adolescence or even earlier—Admiral David Glasgow Farragut began serving as a midshipman in the War of 1812 at the age of 10, and was commanding a prize crew (the sailors put in charge of taking a captured ship into port) at the age of 12. Under such circumstances, jokes and folklore about a handsome young midshipman's supposed sexual availability to other officers were probably inevitable. Nor were they entirely unbounded by fact, as testimony given in the court of inquiry concerning the conduct of one Lieutenant Owen Burns of the frigate USS *Potomac* in 1835 shows. The court questioned ship's boy Andrew Hansen:

> *Question.* Did you ever frig LT Burns?
> *Answer.* Yes.
> *Q.* How often?
> *A.* Five or six times.

We got the syph at Tenerife. Tenerife is one of the islands in the
Canaries, an archipelago in the Atlantic ocean off the northwest coast
of Africa. The Canaries belong to Spain, and have long been important
to sailors. From the time of Columbus on, ships sailing to the New
World would stop at the Canary Islands to replenish their stores. Not
surprisingly, fresh food and water weren't the only things the sailors
brought back on board.

From *Harper's New Monthly Magazine*, October 1858.

CRUISING 'ROUND YARMOUTH

While cruising 'round Yarmouth one day on a spree,
I met a fair damsel, the wind blowing free.
"I'm a fast-going clipper, my kind sir," said she,
"I'm sailing in ballast, my hold is quite free."

> *Chorus:*
> To-ra-li-addy, to-a-lie-ay
> To-ra-li-addy, right to-ra-li-ay.

What country she come from I could not tell which,
But by her appearance I thought she was Dutch:
Her flag bore its colors, her masthead was low,
She was round at the counter and bluff at the bow.

I gave her my hawser, I took her in tow,
And yardarm to yardarm together we'd go.
We chaffed on so lightly, so frisky and gay
'Til we came to an anchor on Ratcliffe Highway.

She took me upstairs to a snug little room
And into her parlor I run my jib boom.

She lowered her topsails, her staysails and all,
With her lily-white hand on me reef-tackle fall.

The watch being ended, I said, "Maid, give o'er—
Betwixt wind and water you've run me ashore.
My shot locker's empty, my powder is spent,
I can't fire a shot for it's choked to the vent."

Cannon in action aboard the *Albemarle*, circa 1864. From *The Century Magazine*, July 1888.

Here's luck to the girl with the black curly locks,
Here's luck to the girl that ran Jack on the rocks,
Here's luck to the doctor who eased all his pain,
He squared his main yards—he's a-cruising again.

Yarmouth. The English town of Yarmouth, in Norfolk, has been a major seaport since the Middle Ages. Once famous for its herring fisheries, Yarmouth is now also a base for North Sea gas and oil exploration.

I'm a fast-going clipper. The clipper ships of the latter half of the nineteenth century were among the most beautiful vessels of the age of sail. With their narrow, streamlined hulls and large spread of sail, they were also for a time the fastest vessels afloat. One American-built clipper, the *Lightning,* set the all-time record for a single day's sail, covering 436 nautical miles in 24 hours. A young lady who is "fast," on the other hand, is in terms of behavior no better than she should be—a prime prospect, in other words, for a sailor lad's entertainment. From this auspicious beginning, the song proceeds through a whole series of nautical puns.

Clipper ship. The schoolship *St. Mary's.* From *St. Nicholas,* July 1903.

I'm sailing in ballast, my hold is quite free. A ship sailing in ballast has no cargo aboard, only the stones or other material kept in the hold to add weight and stabilize the vessel. The young lady likewise is free of entanglements; she has nothing (or no one) aboard her; and her hold is ready to take in a cargo. This is not the only time in nautical literature when a young lady's "hold" is her vagina.

But by her appearance I thought she was Dutch. The rivalry between the English and the Dutch navies was one of long standing. In 1667, during the Second Anglo-Dutch War, the Dutch Admiral Michiel de Ruyter even went so far as to take his ships raiding up the River Medway. The Dutch fleet burned or captured a number of English vessels, including among the latter the Duke of York's own flagship the

"She was round at the counter and bluff at the bow." Fifteenth-century caravels. From *Harper's New Monthly Magazine*, December 1876.

74

Royal Charles, before sailing back downriver and returning to Holland. To this day, the coat-of-arms taken from *Royal Charles*'s stern-quarter is on display in the Ryke Museum in Amsterdam.

Her flag bore its colors. The flag of the Netherlands bears three wide horizontal stripes of red, white, and blue. Prior to about 1630, the uppermost stripe was orange, rather than red, reflecting the colors of the ruling House of Orange. In the nineteenth century, it was often the custom to fly an orange pennant along with the red, white, and blue version of the flag. The young lady herself may be wearing cosmetics—red rouge—which no decent lady would wear, making her a painted hussy. Or perhaps she's wearing a red dress, that is, she's a scarlet woman.

Her masthead was low. The young lady's dress of red, white, and blue (or of orange, white, and blue, or possibly of red, white, blue, and orange) has a low-cut neckline.

She was round at the counter and bluff at the bow. Our sailor's companion of the evening has a nice round ass and ample, well-supported cleavage. In a fishing ship this configuration—rounded at the stern, or rear, end, with a high bow—is typically Dutch; and the proper name for such a vessel is a *hooker*. The term "hooker" can also be applied as an insult (see "boat" and "garbage scow," above) to any vessel, implying that it is past its prime.

Young ladies in song were frequently compared to ships:

> When I get to Liverpool town
> > Fire Maringo, fire him away
> I'll toss a line to little Sally Brown
> > Fire Maringo, fire him away
>
> Sally Brown she's a handy little craft
> > Fire Maringo, fire him away
> Sharp up forward and rounded in the aft
> > Fire Maringo, fire him away

I took her in tow. The sailor offers the young lady his arm, and they walk along side by side ("yardarm to yardarm.")

We chaffed on so lightly. To "chaff" is to rub against something. "Chaffing gear" is the material—rags, canvas, pieces of old fire hose—put on lines to keep them from cutting one another when they rub.

Ratcliffe Highway. Ratcliffe Highway is nowhere near Yarmouth. In fact, some versions of this song don't mention Yarmouth at all. Instead, they start right out with our Jack Tar strolling down Ratcliffe Highway, which ran from London down to the docks, and was part of the same waterfront area as Limehouse and Wapping. The whole area was infamous for its rowdiness. In 1857, J. Ewing Ritchie wrote in "The night side of London":

> Up and down Ratcliffe-highway do the sailors of every country under heaven stroll. . . . They have ploughed the stormy main, they have known the perils of a treacherous sea and of a lee shore—but there are worse perils, and those perils await them in Ratcliffe-highway. . . . There were public-houses here—I know not if the custom prevails now—to which was attached a crew of infamous women; these bring Jack into the house to treat them, but while Jack drinks gin the landlord gives them from another tap water, and then against their sober villainy poor Jack has no chance. I fear many respectable people in this neighbourhood have thus made fortunes. Jack is prone to grog and dancing, and here they meet him at every turn. Women, wild-eyed, boisterous, with cheeks red with rouge and flabby with intemperance, decked out with dresses and ribbons of the gayest hue, are met with by hundreds—all alike equally coarse, and insolent, and unlovely in manners and appearance, but all equally resolved on victimising poor Jack.

Similar practices exist to this day, just as "Hey, sailor, buy me a drink?" is still a common line in seaport bars. There's the old champagne trick, for example, in which the girl asks her escort to buy her a glass of champagne (in reality often ginger ale). Since champagne won't keep once opened, this forces Jack to buy not just one glass, but the entire bottle. And as the editor of this book has had occasion to observe, "You wouldn't believe how many two-hundred-dollar bottles of champagne there are in sleazy waterfront bars."

Into her parlor I run my jib boom. He goes with the young lady into her private quarters. His "jib boom" is possibly his nose (which projects from the face in the manner of a jib boom), since the really explicit sexual imagery comes later in the verse.

Whalebone corset advertisement. From *Godey's Magazine,* September 1895

She lowered her topsails, her staysails, and all. She takes off her blouse and her corset.

Her lily-white hand on me reef-tackle fall. The reef-tackle fall is a line which, when hauled upon, causes the sail to rise up to the yardarm. In some versions, the young lady's hand is on Jack's "gun-tackle fall": a line which, when hauled upon, causes a ship's gun to come into battery, i.e., to protrude from its gunport. In either case, so it also goes with poor Jack. Please note that at sea "tackle" is always pronounced with a long A: *taykle.*

Betwixt wind and water. That portion of the ship which is above the waves (the "water"), but which is not part of the rigging (the "wind"). In Jack's case, an embarrassingly personal area of his anatomy.

I can't fire a shot for it's choked to the vent. Poor Jack is sexually

USS *Essex* with guns protruding. From *Harper's New Monthly Magazine*, August 1859.

exhausted. Judging from the imagery in the last line of the verse, he also is or shortly will be experiencing difficulty in urination and similar unpleasant symptoms. "Choked to the vent" is another term from ship's gunnery: the barrel of the cannon is so full of carbon and sulphur residue that the touchhole can no long give fire to the charge. The "vent" is also the term in venery for an animal's anus.

He squared his main yards—he's a-cruising again. When the yards are not parallel to the deck they are said to be "scandalized." This could be a sign of a slovenly ship. When the yards are squared, once again the vessel is all ship-shape, ready for all winds, and able to sail properly.

Note that the double meaning of "cruising" has persisted over time.

WHAT DO WE DO WITH A DRUNKEN SAILOR?

What do we do with a drunken sailor?
What do we do with a drunken sailor?
What do we do with a drunken sailor
Early in the morning?

Put him in a longboat and row him over,
Put him in a longboat and row him over,

Longboat approaching a ship. From *Harper's New Monthly Magazine*, May 1878.

Put him in a longboat and row him over,
Early in the morning.

Heave him by the balls with a running bowline,
Heave him by the balls with a running bowline,
Heave him by the balls with a running bowline,
Early in the morning

Put him in the bilge and make him drink it,
Put him in the bilge and make him drink it,
Put him in the bilge and make him drink it,
Early in the morning.

Shave his balls with a rusty razor,
Shave his balls with a rusty razor,
Shave his balls with a rusty razor,
Early in the morning.

Put him in the scuppers with a hosepipe on him,
Put him in the scuppers with a hosepipe on him,
Put him in the scuppers with a hosepipe on him,
Early in the morning.

Put him in bed with the captain's daughter,
Put him in bed with the captain's daughter,
Put him in bed with the captain's daughter,
Early in the morning.

Tie him to the taffrail when she's yardarm under,
Tie him to the taffrail when she's yardarm under,
Tie him to the taffrail when she's yardarm under,
Early in the morning.

LIKE "PADDY LAY BACK," this is a capstan shanty, to which an inventive chantyman could extemporize verses as necessary to fit the duration of the task.

Heave him by the balls with a running bowline. To heave on something is to pull or haul on it; a running bowline is a bowline knot used to provide the eye for a running noose. (A running knot is one which moves on the line, as when a noose tightens down.) Our drunken sailor is in for a painful experience, to say the least.

Put him in the bilge and make him drink it. The bilges are the lowest part of the ship inside the hull, and thus a natural collection-point for water from rainfall and from breaking seas. This mixture of salt and fresh water quickly becomes ill-smelling and noxious, not to say completely undrinkable. Even the air in the bilges could be hazardous to a sailor's health. In the seventeenth and eighteenth centuries, the bilges of some older vessels were so poorly ventilated that sailors working in them could succumb to asphyxiation.

Put him in the scuppers with a hosepipe on him. The scuppers are similar to gutters; they run along the sides of the main deck, outboard, to channel water on deck over the side. The hosepipe, connected to the pump, will empty the bilges, or bring up seawater as the case demands.

Pumping sweep attached to a ship's mainmast. From *The Century Magazine*, December 1891.

Tie him to the taffrail when she's yardarm under. The taffrail was the rail around the stern of the ship. Like a great deal of nautical language, the original word was actually Dutch: *tafereel*.

The yardarm is the outboard end of the spar of a square-rigged ship. When a ship is yardarm under, she is rolling heavily, so heavily that the ends of the spars are dipping into the sea. The open poop deck, where the taffrail is located, would be a wet and dangerous place in such foul weather.

Dancing girl showing her legs. From *Harper's New Monthly Magazine*, March 1857.

THE MAID OF AMSTERDAM

In Amsterdam there lived a maid—
Bless you, young women!
In Amsterdam there lived a maid—
Mark well what I do say!
In Amsterdam there lived a maid,
And she was mistress of her trade.
I'll go no more a roving with you, fair maid.

> *Chorus:*
> A-roving, a-roving, since roving's been my ru-i-n,
> I'll go no more a roving with you, fair maid.

I put my hand around her waist—
Bless you, young women!
I put my hand around her waist—
Mark well what I do say!
I put my hand around her waist;
She says. "Young man, you're in some haste."
I'll go no more a-roving with you, fair maid.

I put my hand upon her knee—
Bless you, young women!
I put my hand upon her knee—
Mark well what I do say!
I put my hand upon her knee;
She says, "Young man, you're rather free."
I'll go no more a-roving with you fair maid.

I put my hand upon her thigh—
Bless you, young women!
I put my hand upon her thigh—
Mark well what I do say!
I put my hand upon her thigh;
She says, "Young man, you're rather high."
I'll go no more a-roving with you fair maid.

I put my hand upon her snatch—
Bless you, young women!
I put my hand upon her snatch—
Mark well what I do say!
I put my hand upon her snatch;
She says, "Young man, that's my main hatch."
I'll go no more a-roving with you fair maid.

She rolled me over on my back—
Bless you, young women!
She rolled me over on my back—
Mark well what I do say!
She rolled me over on my back
And fucked me 'til my bollocks cracked.
I'll go no more a-roving with you fair maid.

And when I slipped her on the blocks—
Bless you, young women!

And when I slipped her on the blocks—
Mark well what I do say!
And when I slipped her on the blocks
She says, "Young man, I've got the pox."
I'll go no more a-roving with you fair maid.

And when I'd spent my whole year's pay—
Bless you, young women!
And when I'd spent my whole year's pay—
Mark well what I do say!
And when I'd spent my whole year's pay,
She slipped her line and sailed away.
I'll go no more a-roving with you fair maid.

AMSTERDAM, A PORT IN the Netherlands, had and still has its red-light district. In these days of legal prostitution and readily available latex condoms, however, poor Jack is less likely to get the pox.

This is the Great Pox, or syphilis, not to be confused with smallpox. The pox has had a number of other names. In England it is the French disease. In France it is the Spanish disorder. And so on. No one wants to lay claim to it. The pox appears to have come from the Americas during one of Columbus's first voyages—or from somewhere in Africa and/or Eastern Europe during the dislocations following the final breakup of the Byzantine Empire—or from a less virulent form of the disease already present in Western Europe. In short, the disease's origins remain controversial. What's clear is that sometime during the late fifteenth century syphilis in Europe leaped from being (pick one) an either completely nonexistent or largely unnoticed ailment, all the way to being a major public health problem.

Young man, that's my main hatch. The main hatch is the opening in the ship's main deck that leads to the cargo hold. A "snatch" is a slang term for the feminine pudenda. (*Pudenda* is Latin for "shameful," in case you were interested.)

I slipped her on the blocks. To slip a vessel onto the blocks is to put her into drydock, where she is at rest and no longer moving up and down and side to side and back and forth. Jack and the young lady, their amorous activity completed, have settled down in bed for a night's sleep, and have reached the pillow talk stage.

She slipped her line and sailed away. A ship that has slipped her line has departed by stealth or in haste, without informing linehandling parties or the dockmaster, leaving her mooring line still attached to the pier. The young lady has similarly departed while Jack was sleeping.

From *The Century Magazine*, April 1892.

BELL BOTTOM TROUSERS

Once there was a serving maid, down in Kerry Lane.
Her mistress was kind and her master was the same.
'Til along came a sailor ashore on liberty,
And he was the cause of all her misery.

> *Chorus:*
> With his bell bottom trousers and coat of navy blue,
> He will climb your rigging like his daddy used to do.

He asked her for a candle to light his way to bed,
He asked her for a kerchief to tie around his head.
Then the pretty serving maid, thinking it no harm,
Got in beside him just to keep the sailor warm.

She lifted up the covers and a moment there did lie;
He was on her, he was in her in the twinkling of an eye.
He was on her, he was in her, he was plowing up a storm,
And the only word she thought to say—"I hope you're
  keeping warm!'

Early next morning, right outside the door,
The sailor left a letter and this was what it bore:
"Oh, you may have a daughter or you may have a son—
Here's five pounds for the damage I have done.

DOUGLAS MORGAN

Now if you have a daughter, then bounce her on your knee,
But if you have a son send the bastard out to sea.
With his bell bottom trousers and coat of navy blue,
He will climb the rigging like his daddy used to do."

The moral of this story is very plain to see:
Never trust a sailor an inch above your knee.
For if you trust a sailor, when he puts out to sea
He'll leave you with a bastard to bounce upon your knee.

"Never trust a sailor." From *St. Nicholas,* June 1901.

What Do You Do with a Drunken Sailor?

NOT ALL ADVENTURES ashore end up in trouble for the sailor involved. In this ballad, Jack has a fine time; instead, it's the innocent servant girl who gets herself in trouble.

Wide-legged or bell-bottomed trousers have long been part of a sailor's distinctive dress. The style has survived because of its practicality: bell-bottomed trousers are easier than straight-legged ones to take off and put on again when they're damp, and they're easier to roll up if the wearer is going to be standing or wading in water. In their dress version, as part of the classic "sailor suit," they accentuate the wearer's broad shoulders and narrow hips, and are reliably regarded as a serious babe magnet.

A fashionable young lady. From *Godey's Magazine*, September 1895.

THE FIRESHIP

As I stepped out one evening upon a night's career,
I spied a lofty clipper ship and after her I steered.
I hoisted up my signals, which she so quickly knew
And when she saw my signals she immediately hove to.

Chorus:
She had a dark and roving eye
And her hair hung down in ringalets.
She was a nice and proper girl,
One of the rakish kind.

"O sailor, please excuse me for being out so late,
But if my parents knew of it, oh, sad would be my fate.
My father is a minister, a good and honest man;
My mother is a Methodist; and I do the best I can."

I eyed that girl both up and down, for I'd heard such talk
    before,
And when she moored herself to me I knew she was a
    whore.
But still she was a pretty girl, she'd shyly hung her head,
"I'll go along with you, my lad," to me these words she
    said.

I took her to a nice hotel, I knew she wouldn't mind;
But little did I ever think she was of the rakish kind.
I played with her for quite some time, and learned to my
  surprise
She was nothing but a fireship rigged up in a disguise.

So up the stairs and into bed I took that maiden fair.
I fired off my cannon into her thatch of hair.
I fired off my broadside until my shot was spent,
Then rammed that fireship's waterline until my ram was
  bent.

Then in the morning she was gone, my money was gone too,
My clothes she'd hocked, my watch she stole, my seabag
  was gone too.
She'd left behind a souvenir, I'd have you all to know,
And in nine days' time, to my surprise, there was fire down
  below.

Now all you jolly sailormen who sail upon the sea
From England to America, take warning now by me.
Beware of lofty fireships, they'll be the ruin of you,
They'll empty your shot locker and pick your pocket too.

EARLIEST RECORDED DATE 1612; over three centuries later, this song
reached popularity in bowdlerized form in the early 1950s when the
Weavers sang it as "Her Hair Hung Down in Ringlets."

"Yea, stranger engines for the brunt of war than was the fiery keel at
Antwerp's bridge I'll cause my servile spirits to invent," says Dr.
Faustus in Christopher Marlowe's play—a topical reference to then-
new military technology. Fireships, in the sense of derelict vessels set

on fire and allowed to float toward the enemy, had been used in warfare since ancient times. With the advent of gunpowder, it wasn't long before some genius thought to combine black powder, a slow match, and a wooden ship, thus turning a fireship from a floating bonfire into a floating bomb. Fireships were successfully employed against the Duke of Parma by the defenders of Antwerp in 1585 and by the British against the Spanish Armada in 1588 (and still later by the Dutch against the English in the raid up the Medway).

It didn't take sailors long to see and make use of the fireship's metaphorical possibilities. Gonorrhea, not syphilis, is the disease in question here. Gonorrhea causes a painful burning in the male urethra, especially when urinating; modern prostitutes check for the disease in their clients by squeezing the organ and looking for the typical milky discharge. Wily sailors, in their turn, check their ladies with a RealLemon squeezebulb of lemon juice, which supposedly will reveal if the lady has any open sores in her nether regions.

A fire ship. From *Harper's New Monthly Magazine*, June 1859.

Contemporary Navy customs and folklore still frequently involve venerial diseases, such as PCOD announcemants and the mythical Black Island. The PCOD is the Pussy Cut-Off Date—the last day of a cruise on which a sailor can catch VD, have the symptoms appear, and have the corpsman cure it before he gets back to homeport and has to explain to his wife/girlfriend about a nasty condition in a delicate spot. Sometimes it's announced over the 1MC (the ship's general announcing system: "For the information of all hands, today is the PCOD." Sometimes it's listed in the POD (Plan of the Day). Sometimes it's just noised about (generally the word is started by the corpsman). It's both practical and cynical.

Black Island is where sailors get sent if they catch Black Syph. Black Syph is a terrible disease (so the rumor runs), an antibiotic-resistant version of syphilis which, so far, has not reached CONUS (the continental U.S.). In order to keep things that way, if you catch Black Syph, you're sent to Black Island for the rest of your short, unhappy life, while your family is told that you died in an accident—washed over the side in a storm, perhaps. The exact location of Black Island is unknown, but it's probably somewhere very hot.

One of the rakish kind. A nautical pun: "rakish" refers to the young lady's dashing and unconventional (and probably persuadable) air; it also refers to a ship's masts, which are said to be "raked" when they slant backwards—sometimes by as much as 15 to 17 degrees—from the perpendicular. A ship with raked masts is one built for speed and fast maneuvering; so might our sailor lad hope to find his young lady.

But "rake" also has another, more ominous nautical meaning. In ship-to-ship combat, the most telling blow one ship can strike on another is to "cross the T"—sail at right angles to the enemy's course, in such a way that all of the cannon along one side of the ship are able to fire into the enemy at once, while the enemy is unable to respond with anything except bow or stern cannons. To fire such a broadside at the enemy is to "rake" them; the cannon shot, traveling down the entire length of the enemy ship, will cause great devastation. The frigate USS *Chesapeake*, in her battle with HMS *Shannon*, was hit by a raking broadside in the first minutes of the engagement, killing or mortally wounding nearly everyone on the quarterdeck, including the

The frigate *Boston* raking *Le Berceau*. From *The Century Magazine,* November 1890.

captain, the first lieutenant, and the sailors at the wheel. *Chesapeake* struck her colors soon afterward.

My father is a minister. The young lady being a minister's daughter is no defense for poor Jack, for all that she is apparently pure, sweet, and innocent. She also isn't the only young lady in folksong to make the claim. In "The Wayward Boy", the heroine says, (to the tune of "Brighton Camp," AKA "The Girl I Left Behind Me"):

> "My father is a minister,
> My maidenhead does cherish,
> So every night he locks me tight,
> So horny that I perish."

And as the cowboy hero of "The Old Chisholm Trail" says:

I reached in my pocket and I pulled out a quarter.
Says she 'Young man, I'm a minister's daughter.' "

Later the cowboy finds himself in the same predicament as poor Jack Tar:

I went to the doc 'cause my prick was sore.
"By God," says the doc, "it's the same damn whore."

Later, during the Korean War, an American soldier discovers the same truth, to the tune of "On Top Of Old Smokey":

I ran to the medic,
Screamed, "What shall I do?"
The doc was dumbfounded;
Old Smokey was blue.

My mother is a Methodist. Methodists were renowned for their religious enthusiasm and straitlaced morality, just as sailors were known for their roving and licentious lifestyle. In song, at least, the two forces were bound to collide.

And when she moored herself to me I knew she was a whore. A ship is moored when it is no longer underway, but is attached in some fashion to a pier, or another ship, or a mooring buoy. In similar fashion, the young lady has attached herself to poor Jack.

THE BANKS OF NEWFOUNDLAND

You bully boys of Liverpool,
I'll have you all beware:
When you sail on them packet ships,
No dungaree jumpers wear,
But have a big monkey jacket
All ready to your hand,
For there blow some cold nor'westers
On the banks of Newfoundland.

> *Chorus:*
> We'll wash her and we'll scrub her
> With holy stone and sand,
> For there blow some cold nor'westers
> On the banks of Newfoundland.

The mate he stood on the fo'c'sle head,
And loudly he did roar,
"Come rattle her in, me lucky lads,
We're bound for America's shore!
Wash the mud from the dead man's face,
And haul or you'll be damned!

There blow some cold nor'westers
On the banks of Newfoundland."

It's now we're watch-and-watch, me lads,
With the decks all covered in snow.
But soon we'll see the pay table
And we'll spend the whole night below.
And on the docks, come down in flocks,
Those pretty girls they stand,
Saying, "It's better with me than it is at sea
On the banks of Newfoundland."

When you sail on them packet ships. After the Napoleonic era ended with the Congress of Vienna in 1815, the Atlantic Ocean ceased to be a theater of war. For the first time, unarmed merchant ships could make the crossing in no danger except for that which came from the sea itself. What followed was the era of the "packet ships"—commercial

The Shipwreck, from a painting by Joseph Mallord William Turner. From *Harper's New Monthly Magazine,* February 1878.

vessels that took their name from the packets of mail they carried between Britain and America. The Black Ball line, later made famous in "Blow the Man Down" and other shanties, was the first to begin regular service.

What was new and innovative about the packet ships was that they adhered to a schedule. Prior to 1818 and the commencement of packet service, ships waited in port until they had a full cargo of goods and passengers before sailing. The packets, in contrast, sold not only cargo space, but also speed and reliability. These commodities, however, came at a high human price: Discipline on the packet ships was harsh and brutal, enforced by hard captains and "bucko mates" who kept the crew in order with knotted rope "starters" and rattan staves, and even with their fists if necessary.

Dungaree jumpers. Cotton jackets. The word comes from the Hindi *dungrl*, meaning canvas. Such a jacket would be excellent for voyages in tropical waters, being both lightweight and sturdy; in the freezing cold and wet of the high North Atlantic, it would be disastrous. Jack Tar needs to purchase a "monkey jacket," or "pea coat," made of heavy wool. ("Pea," here, is derived from the Dutch word *pij*, meaning "short.")

For there blow some cold nor'westers / On the banks of Newfoundland. Off the coast of southeastern Newfoundland lies a dangerously stormy area of the North Atlantic known as the Grand Banks. The chilly Labrador Current flows across the Banks while the tropic-warmed Gulf Stream flows along their eastern side, and the confluence of warm and cold water over this relatively shallow ground—about 120 to 600 feet—breeds dense fog, high winds, and heavy seas. The same conditions are ideal for the development of plankton, making the Banks a rich fishing ground shared by fleets out of Canada, New England, Portugal, and other seafaring nations. The Grand Banks also lie along the route followed by the packet ships on their voyages between England and America

Holy stone and sand. "Holy stone," in the form of pumice blocks shaped like bibles, was used with sand to clean the wooden decks. Sailors had to kneel to do the job.

The mate he stood on the fo'c'sle head. The "fo'c'sle head" could be any of several places on the ship's bow, or forecastle. The forecastle, pronounced fo'c'sle, was originally the "forward castle," a term harking back to the Middle Ages—this would have been the part of the ship that held its fighting soldiers. The reference in the song may refer to one of the catheads, horizontal beams to which the anchors are lashed when underway; or it may refer to the "head," the ship's toilet. The head is constantly washed by waves. In days of sail the wind always came from astern, making this a natural place to relieve oneself—then as now, "don't piss into the wind" is excellent advice. (Sailors would also keep barrels of urine on deck in which to wash their clothes, first to kill the lice and second to bleach the cloth. After being washed in urine, the clothing would be trailed astern tied to lengths of small stuff to rinse them out.)

Wash the mud from the dead man's face. This refers to using a hosepipe to wash the mud from the ship's anchor as it is being brought aboard and made fast to the catheads. An anchor is sometimes called a "mudhook."

It's now we're watch-and-watch. Watch-and-watch refers to standing watch four hours on and four hours off, 'round the clock. Done for long periods, this is exhausting—but not as brutal as "four on and carry on," where nobody goes off watch at all until the crisis is over.

Ship's forecastle. From *Scribner's Magazine*, May 1888.

THE HANDSOME CABIN BOY

It's of a pretty fair maid, as you shall understand.
She had a mind for roving unto a foreign land.
Attired in sailor's clothing she boldly did appear
And engaged with the captain for to serve him for a year.

She engaged with the captain a cabin boy to be.
The wind it was in favor, and they soon put out to sea.
The captain's lady being on board, she seemed it to enjoy,
So glad the captain had engaged a handsome cabin boy.

The captain's wife, she being on board, she seemed in great joy
To think her husband had engaged such a handsome cabin boy.
And now and then she'd slip him a kiss, and she would 'a
    liked to toy;
But 'twas the captain found the secret out of the handsome
    cabin boy.

Her cheeks appeared like roses, and with her side-locks
    curled,
The sailors ofttimes smiled and said, "He looks just like a
    girl!"
But eating captain's biscuit her color did destroy,

DOUGLAS MORGAN

And the waist did swell on pretty Nell, the handsome cabin
  boy.

As through the Bay of Biscay their gallant ship did plow,
One night among the sailors there was a pretty row.
They bundled from their hammocks, it did their rest destroy,
And they swore about the groaning of the handsome cabin
  boy.

From *The Century Magazine*, November 1889.

"O doctor, O doctor," the cabin boy did cry.
The sailors swore by all that's good, the cabin boy would die.
The doctor ran with all his might and smiling at the fun,
To think a sailor lad should have a daughter or a son.

The sailors when they heard the joke they all began to stare.
The child belonged to none of them, they solemnly did
swear.
The captain's wife, she says to him, "My dear, I wish you
joy—
For it's either you or me's betrayed the handsome cabin
boy!"

So each man took his tot of rum, and he drunk success to
trade,
And likewise to the cabin boy who was neither man nor
maid.
Here's hoping the wars don't rise again, our sailors to
destroy,
And here's hoping for a jolly lot more like the handsome
cabin boy.

BRINGING FEMALES ON BOARD ship wasn't unknown in the days of sail, and more than one sea-captain brought his wife along with him on a voyage. The wives were often navigators, since they had both the free time on shipboard and the schooling that their husbands—many of whom had been going to sea since childhood—perhaps lacked. In 1856, Mary Patten, the wife of Captain Joshua Patten of the clipper ship *Neptune's Car*, was forced to take charge of the ship when her husband collapsed with "brain fever" on a run from New York to San Francisco around Cape Horn. Mary Patten was 19 and pregnant at the time, but she knew navigation, and saw the ship and its cargo safely around the

From *The Century Magazine*, February 1890.

Horn. When she steered *Neptune's Car* into harbor in San Francisco, she noted in the ship's log that the voyage had taken 136 days.

In the whaling chanty "Ranzo," the shanghaied tailor turned whale-fisherman Reuben Ranzo achieves social mobility after winning the affections of the captain's daughter:

> She gave him rum and water,
> Ranzo, boys, Ranzo!
> And a bit more than she oughter,
> Ranzo, me boys, Ranzo!

She gave him education,
And taught him navigation.

She made him the best sailor
On board that New York whaler.

He married the captain's daughter
And still sails on salt water.

Now Ranzo he's a sailor,
Ranzo, boys, Ranzo!
He's Captain of that whaler,
Ranzo, me boys, Ranzo!

Even ships of war sometimes had females on board. The phrase "Show a leg!" sung out by the boatswain when getting the men out of their hammocks was to show the gender of the person sleeping there. Women wouldn't be expected to heave out, trice up, and turn to.

The ultimate outcome of our handsome cabin boy's adventures wasn't entirely unheard-of either. In 1803, while the frigate USS *Chesapeake* was on the Mediterranean Station, the wife of a sailor named Low actually did give birth. As Midshipman Henry Wadsworth recorded in his journal, "The other ladies of the Bay—The Foreward most part of the Birth [sic] Deck—viz. Mrs. Watson: the Boatswain's wife, Mrs. Myres the Carpenter's Lady—with Mrs. Crosby the Corporal's lady: got drunk in their own Quarters out of pure spite—not being invited to celebrate the Christening of Melancthon Woolsey Low."

Although naval regulations strictly forbade the men from taking women on board, the senior petty officers apparently were able to do so in a clandestine manner, although exactly how secret it was is up to interpretation. *Chesapeake* fired a full broadside in order to help out Mrs. Low's delivery, an event that the captain of the ship could hardly have failed to notice.

From *The Century Magazine*, March 1892.

BLOW THE MAN DOWN

Oh, blow the man down, bullies, blow the man down,
Way aye blow the man down!
Oh, blow the man down, bullies, blow him away—
Give me some time to blow the man down.

As I was a walking down Paradise Street
Way aye blow the man down
A pretty young damsel I chanced for to meet.
Give me some time to blow the man down!

She was round in the counter and bluff in the bow,
Way aye blow the man down
So I took in all sail and cried, "Way enough now."
Give me some time to blow the man down!

So I tailed her my flipper and took her in tow
Way aye blow the man down
And yardarm to yardarm away we did go.
Give me some time to blow the man down!

But as we were going she said unto me
Way aye blow the man down

"There's a spanking full-rigger just ready for sea."
Give me some time to blow the man down!

But as soon as that packet was clear of the bar
Way aye blow the man down
The mate knocked me down with the end of a spar.
Give me some time to blow the man down!

It's starboard and larboard on deck you will sprawl
Way aye blow the man down
For Kicking Jack Williams commands the Black Ball.
Give me some time to blow the man down!

Docks at Cardiff. From *Harper's New Monthly Magazine*, February 1877.

So I give you fair warning before we belay,
Way aye blow the man down
Don't ever take heed of what pretty girls say.
Give me some time to blow the man down!

OVER THE PASSAGE OF TIME, this song has become more or less permanently associated with Liverpool and the packet ships. "Blow the man down" refers to striking a man so hard that he falls to the deck. The packets, with their need for adhering to fixed schedules, kept a brutal discipline.

So I took in all sail and cried, "Way enough now." Jack, having spied a young lady, stops to talk with her. Taking in sail is a maneuver for slowing and stopping a ship—"Way enough now" means "I'm going fast enough now."

When the clipper *Red Jacket* came into Liverpool in 1854 after a record-breaking trans-Atlantic run, Captain Asa Eldridge of Yarmouth, Massachusetts showed the locals how it was done:

> "Outside the port tugs had offered to tow the clipper, but she was going so fast they could never have kept their hawsers taut. She shot ahead, leaving them to wallow in her wake. The *Red Jacket* swept into Mersey with everything drawing, presenting a spectacle of surpassing grandeur. Cheers burst from the thousands on shore. Then Captain Asa Eldridge gave them a thrill they least expected—he took in his kites, his skysails, royals and top gallants, hung his courses, or lower sails, in their gear, ignored the tugs that caught up, and, throwing the Red Jacket into the wind, helm hard down, he backed her long side of berth without aid, while the crew took in sail with a celerity that seemed like magic to the spectators—a superb piece of seamanship."

But as we were going she said unto me / "There's a spanking full-rigger just ready for sea." Following the lead of a beautiful young lady has gotten more than one young sailor into trouble he had not anticipated. A sailor of the editor's acquaintance once went bowling in New York City with a number of his shipmates. At some point in the evening, he struck up an acquaintance with a young lady in a tight blue sweater—his friends never learned her name, but all of them remembered the sweater—and left the bowling alley in her company. He didn't return to the ship that night. In fact, he wasn't heard from until two days later, when he telephoned the ship, much chastened, to explain that he was flat broke in Cleveland, Ohio, and didn't have the faintest idea how he'd gotten there.

The mate knocked me down with the end of a spar. Discipline on board the packet ships was swift and physical. The first mate stood ready at all times to back up the captain's orders with a rope's end, a stick of rattan, or his fists. As the chanty "Leave Her, Johnny," says about another ship:

From *The Century Magazine*, December 1891.

The mate was a bucko an' the Old Man a Turk,
  Leave her, Johnny, Leave her!
The bosun was a bugger with the middle name o' Work.
  And it's time for us to leave her!

It's starboard and larboard on deck you will sprawl. Larboard is the older, alternate term for the port side of the ship (the left-hand side as you face forward.) It comes from the Middle English *laddebord,* referring to the side of the ship which is next to the dock for loading and unloading cargo. *Starboard*—right as you face forward—comes from Old English *steorbord,* referring to the side of the ship on which the steering oar (the precursor to the rudder, and later the ship's wheel) is mounted.

Kicking Jack Williams commands the Black Ball. The Black Ball Line was the first and most famous of the packet lines; other lines included the Red Cross and Swallow Tail Lines. "Kicking Jack Williams" isn't an atypical nickname for a packetship captain—boots worked as well as fists for enforcing discipline.

Fleas in action. From *Harper's New Monthly Magazine*, July 1859.

GUANTANAMO BAY

Guantanamo Bay, call it Gitmo for short,
Not much of a base and far less of a port—
One look at the piers and you'll know that you're seein'
The goddamdest hole in the whole Caribbean.

So hurrah then for Gitmo, on Cuba's fair shore,
The home of the cockroach, the flea, and the whore.
We'll sing of its praises and wait for the day
We get the hell out of Guantanamo Bay.

In Guantanamo Bay we're confined to our quarters,
We're scratching and sweating, we're waiting for orders,
We're watching the bay and surveying the wrecks
And wondering which we'll be shipping on next.

When the cruiser *Alaska* hove into view
To clean off her bottom and pick up a crew,
Nary a sailor was ready for sea—
They'd all been on leave and they all had VD.

Guantanamo City has hundreds of doors,
And behind every one there are hundreds of whores.

They lean on the windows with stark naked chests
And beat out your brains with their low-hanging breasts.

My buddies and I have a hell of a plan—
We're saving each nickel and dime that we can.
We'll buy TNT and then one sunny day
We'll blow up this goddam Guantanamo Bay.

Sung to the tune of "The Irish Washer Woman."

Guantanamo Bay. Guantanamo Bay, located in Cuba's Oriente Province on the island's southeast corner, is America's oldest overseas Naval Base. The United States government originally leased the 45 square miles of land and water from the Cuban government in 1903, for use as a coaling station—a base where coal could be stored on-shore in bunkers to refuel visiting ships. (It was the need for coaling stations to support the United States' increasing naval operations in the Pacific that led to American bases in Hawaii, and to the American presence on Wake, Guam, and Midway, as well as in the Philippines.) The treaty and the lease were renewed in 1934, under terms which required that the United States and Cuba mutually consent to terminate the lease. The lease payments were set at $2,000 in gold ($4,085 in current dollars) per year. At the time of the Cuban Revolution of 1958–59 the lease was still in force; in 1962 Fidel Castro accused the United States of "territorial interference" and demanded that the base be given up immediately. The United States government refused, citing the "mutual consent" clause in the lease, and President Kennedy sent Marines to defend the base. Since then, the United States has continued to send the annual lease payments, Cuba has refused to accept them, and Guantanamo Bay remains the only United States military base located in a Communist country.

These days, Guantanamo is used by the Navy for REFTRA—"refresher training." When ships come out of the yards, or when they are first commissioned, their first port of call is often Gitmo, where the crew spends several weeks learning how to go to general quarters, weigh anchor, fire the guns, and perform all the other tasks necessary for the smooth operation of the ship. The base at Guantanamo Bay has also been used periodically over the years to house prisoners and refugees.

Call it Gitmo for short. The Naval abbreviation for Guantanamo Bay, as used in messages and orders, is GTMO.

Not much of a base and far less of a port. Gitmo is a hot, dry, sandy patch of land with a mediocre harbor, and even in pre-Castro days it was a long way from the inviting fleshpots of Havana. It has never been beloved of the sailors and marines who pass through there. (In the Fleet it's well known that NAVY stands for "Never Again Volunteer Yourself." Sailors have less favorable things to say about the Marines, claiming that USMC stands for "Uncle Sam's Misguided Children." A typical intra-service joke: You know the difference between the Marine Corps and the Boy Scouts? The Boy Scouts have adult leadership.)

The cruiser Alaska. The USS *Alaska* (CB-1), in commission 1944–47, made her only port visit to Gitmo in June of 1944.

They'd all been on leave and they all had VD. The loss of potential manpower to venereal disease—always an hazard for sailors bent on

Cuban boat landing, circa 1895. From *Godey's Magazine*, September 1895.

enjoying liberty with the friendly young women of New York, Yarmouth, Valparaiso, and similar lively ports of call—posed a serious problem for the Navy during World War II. Measures to combat the threat, besides the deployment of the newly developed antibiotic penicillin, included changing the regulations so that the mere fact of having VD was no longer an offense, but that having VD and failing to report it was. (Interestingly enough, one of the moving forces behind the change was Eliot Ness, of gangster-era Chicago "the Untouchables" fame, in his World War II job with the Federal Social Protection Program, established to fight venereal disease.)

Guantanamo City has hundreds of doors, And behind every one there are hundreds of whores. This allegation is also heard about Olongopo in the Philippines, and echoes an older English song on a similar subject:

> At Watkins' Town end, at Watkins' Town end,
> At every door there stands a whore
> At Watkins' Town end.

Olongopo is a city outside of the now-disestablished US Naval base at Subic Bay, and has itself been immortalized in bawdy song (to the tune of Sgt. Barry Sadler's "Ballad of the Green Berets"):

> Got no tits upon her chest;
> She is one of Subic's best.
> One hundred men she'll screw today,
> But only two the normal way.

After Castro's revolution in 1958–59, Guantanamo City and its hundreds of doors became off-limits to American personnel (though rumor has it that Marines could still obtain blow jobs from enterprising young women through the holes in the chain-link fence surrounding the base.) Between this and the reference to the 1944 visit of USS *Alaska*, the song's date of original composition can be fixed fairly closely. It was still in oral circulation as recently as the mid-1970s, when the editor of this collection learned it at Gitmo.

From *St. Nicholas,* June 1902.

From *St. Nicholas,* October 1902.

THE CAPTAIN

The captain stormed into the wardroom
And threatened to lower the boom:
"I don't mind the guests in the movies,
But who laid that broad in my room?"

    Chorus:
    Singing mush mush mush toorilayadee
    Mush mush mush toorilayday
    Mush mush mush toorilayadee
    Mush mush mush toorilayday.

The officers' head is communal,
The captain he has a commode.
His bowels aren't a fucking bit looser,
But his pride it swells up like a toad.

The officers ride in the motorboat,
The captain he rides in his gig.
It don't go a fucking bit faster
But it makes the old bastard feel big.

The officers sleep in their hammocks,
The captain he sleeps in his bed.

He don't sleep a fucking bit better,
But he's forty feet nearer the head.

The officers ride in the motorboat,
The admiral he rides in his barge.
He don't go a fucking bit faster;
It just makes the old bastard feel large.

At the officers' club on Tulagi,
The captain won't drink with the boys.
He don't get a fucking bit drunker,
The old bastard just can't stand the noise.

We're always at General Quarters.
The captain he sits at his desk,
And issues the Goddamnest orders
On how all the men should be dressed.

We may have lost one or two battles
And a ship in the midst of a storm,
But there's one thing that you can be sure of—
Our men were in full uniform.

The captain stormed into the wardroom. The wardroom on a navy ship is the officers' common-room.

The officers ride in the motorboat, The captain he rides in his gig. The officers' motorboat and the captain's gig (and for that matter, the admiral's barge in the later verse) are in all likelihood the same physical boat. The difference lies in who is aboard and what ornament is at the top of the detachable flagstaff at the stern. The flagstaff of the captain's gig has a ball ornament at the top; that of the admiral's barge has a stylized halberd. The actual purpose of the various ornaments (there are others for the President, for ambassadors, for the Chief of Naval

Operations, and so on) is so that the officer on the quarterdeck of the ship being approached can see from a distance who—or at least what— is arriving, and can get ready to muster the sideboys, ring the appropriate number of bells, fetch the bosun's mate to pipe the visitor aboard if required, and in general provide all those marks of respect that admirals get upset if they don't have.

Sailors manning a gardner gun. From *The Century Magazine*, October 1888.

The officers sleep in their hammocks. This line suggests that the original song was composed by someone serving aboard a World War II-era destroyer, where—space being at a premium and comfort not—most of the officers and crew were still sleeping in hammocks. Even in the late 1970s, hammocks were still in use aboard some vessels; the editor of this collection recalls sleeping in a hammock aboard a berthing barge in the Brooklyn Navy Yard.

We may have lost one or two battles / And a ship in the midst of a storm. This second line of this verse is probably a reference to the events of December 17–18, 1944, when the ships of Task Force 38— seven fleet and six light carriers, eight battleships, 15 cruisers, and about 50 destroyers—were overtaken by a violent typhoon in the Philippine Sea east of Luzon. Three destroyers, USS *Hull*, USS *Spence*,

HEDGEHOG.—*Erindæus Europæus.*

Hedgehog. From Wood's Natural History, circa 1850.

and USS *Monaghan*, capsized and went down with practically all hands, while a cruiser, five aircraft carriers, and three destroyers suffered serious damage. Approximately 790 officers and men were lost or killed, with another 80 injured. (The 1944 typhoon also plays an important role in another literary work in the seafaring tradition, Herman Wouk's *The Caine Mutiny*.)

At the officers' club on Tulagi. Tulagi is an island in the British Solomons, captured as part of the Guadalcanal campaign in 1942. By 1944, there was in fact an officers' club on Tulagi.

From internal evidence—the references to hammocks, the 1944 hurricane, and Tulagi—this song was most likely composed and sung by junior officers during World War II. The editor of this collection learned it in the mid-1980s from a naval aviator lieutenant (or, to use the traditional term, a "fucking Airedale").

Floating stanzas that frequently show up in addition to the main text include:

> In the progress of civilization
> From anthropoid apes down to man,
> The palm is awarded the Navy
> For frigging whatever it can.

> Exhaustive experimentation
> By Darwin and Huxley and Hall
> Has proved that the ass of the hedgehog
> Can hardly be buggered at all.

> We therefore believe our conclusion
> Is incontrovertibly shown:
> Comparative safety on shipboard
> Is enjoyed by the hedgehog alone.

As well as the follow-up reply:

> Then why don't they do it at Spithead
> Like they do it at Harvard and Yale,
> And likewise at Oxford and Cambridge,
> By shaving the spines off its tail?

(Spithead is one of the main ports used by the British Royal Navy, roughly equivalent in importance and notoriety to Norfolk or San Diego for the American Navy.)

This song goes to the tune of "Botany Bay," also known as "My God, How the Money Rolls In," and floating verses from that song also sometimes attach themselves to the text:

> My father's a street missionary;
> He saves little girlies from sin.
> He'll save you a blonde for a dollar—
> My God, how the money rolls in.